Flo
of th

written by
Janice Emily Bowers

illustrations by
Brian Wignall

Library of Congress Cataloging-in-Publication Data
Bowers, Janice Emily.
Flowers and shrubs of the Mojave Desert / written by
Janice Emily Bowers; illustrations by Brian Wignall.
p.cm.
Includes bibliographical references and index.
ISBN 1–877856–79–7
1. Wild flowers—California—Mojave Desert—Identification.
2. Shrubs—California—Mojave Desert—Identification.
3. Wild flowers—California—Mojave Desert—Pictorial works.
4. Shrubs—California—Mojave Desert—Pictorial works.
5. Botanical illustration. I. Title.

QK149.B676 1998
582.13'09794'95—dc21
98–46900 CIP

221 N. Court
Tucson, AZ 85701
www.spma.org

Net proceeds from SPMA publications
support educational and research programs
in the National Park Service.

Editorial by Derek Gallagher
Design by Mo Martin
Photography: Randy Prentice, cover; Jeff Gnass, page 7;
Larry Ulrich, pages 8-9, 10-11, 12-13; Jack Dykinga, page 14.
Prepress color preparation by Hollis Digital Imaging, Inc.
Printed by Courier Graphics, Inc.

Contents

COVER: Dune evening primrose, *Oenothera deltoides*. Photo by Randy Prentice.

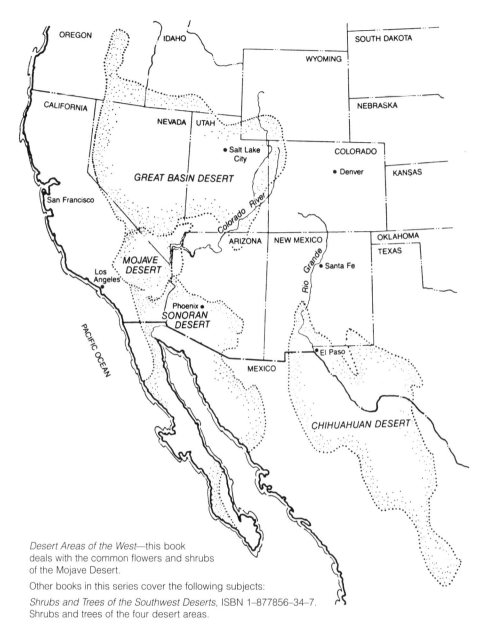

Desert Areas of the West—this book
deals with the common flowers and shrubs
of the Mojave Desert.

Other books in this series cover the following subjects:

Shrubs and Trees of the Southwest Deserts, ISBN 1–877856–34–7.
Shrubs and trees of the four desert areas.

Shrubs and Trees of the Southwest Uplands, ISBN 0–911408–41–X. Shrubs and trees of the
drainages of the upper portion of the Rio Grande and Pecos Rivers; and by the Colorado River
south of Grand Junction, Colorado, and its tributaries the Gunnison, San Juan, and Little Colorado.
We use the 4,500-foot contour to define the beginning of the uplands.

Flowers of the Southwest Mountains, ISBN 0–911408–61–4. Mountain flowers of Arizona, New
Mexico, Colorado, and Utah, starting at 7,000 feet in the Transition Life Zone.

Flowers of the Southwest Deserts, ISBN 0–911408–65–7. Flowers of the Chihuahuan, Sonoran, and
Mojave Deserts.

2

The Mojave Desert and Its Plants

If the arid lands of North America were contiguous, they would cover an area about the size of Alaska, or twice that of Texas. Biotic communities do not recognize political boundaries, however, and the great North American desert sprawls over sixteen states and two countries. The Mojave Desert, being smaller than Ohio, occupies only seven percent of this territory, yet offers a diversity of habitats and plant life, from salt pans where nothing has grown for a thousand years to mesa tops where blackbrushes are so thick that you cannot walk a straight line. The Mojave Desert has sand dunes three hundred feet tall. It has springs where tiny endemic fish play tag among the reeds and rushes. Although the flora includes few trees (other than the so-called Joshua trees whose wildly branching arms provide little in the way of shade but much in terms of habitat for wildlife), no knowledgeable person thinks of the Mojave Desert as poor in plant life. Between one and two thousand species of plants can be found in the Mojave Desert; among them are a number of cacti, many kinds of shrubs, several sorts of parasitic plants, and a huge variety of wildflowers.

One reason for this diversity is the wide variety of substrates, that is, rock types. Sedimentary, igneous, and metamorphic rocks of many kinds are well represented in the Mojave Desert, and it is not unknown for certain species of plants to grow only on particular rock types. The basic equation is that more kinds of rock equal more kinds of plants. Variety in climate is another reason. As in all deserts, the defining climatic feature of the Mojave Desert is scanty and irregular precipitation. Rain is not uniformly distributed across the desert, and because annual totals vary from as little as one or two inches per year in one part of the desert to ten or eleven inches in another, plants with different moisture requirements can find a suitable place to grow. The same is true with temperature. Naturally, daily temperatures range from torrid in summer to downright cold in winter, and a camper who swelters under a mere bedsheet in July will be grateful for a thick down sleeping bag in January. Moreover, temperature follows elevation in a general way, and because the Mojave Desert ranges in elevation from 280 feet below sea level to 4,000 feet above sea level, plants have yet another dimension along which to sort themselves out. Thus, more kinds of climates also equal more kinds of plants.

In most years, the Mojave Desert receives most of its rain in winter. This simple fact is the single most important factor in determining when the desert blooms. Annual wildflowers—plants that go through their entire life cycle in less than a year—are mostly spring bloomers. The seeds germinate with winter rains, forming leafy rosettes that lie flat on the ground. With warming temperatures in spring, the rosettes bolt, just like lettuce plants in a vegetable garden, sending up flower stalks. According to species, flowering lasts a few days or weeks, then fruits take the place of flowers. After the fruits ripen and spill their seeds, the entire plant dies. The seeds remain on the ground and in the soil. Next winter, if the rains are heavy enough, they will germinate, and the cycle will repeat itself. If rains are too light, the seeds are capable of waiting for a good long time, four or five years or even more.

A person who lives for a long time in the Mojave Desert will see many springtimes come and go, and maybe one in five will bring a good wildflower display—what aficionados call "a good spring." All bad springs are more or less alike in that wildflowers are scarce or not to be seen, but all good years are different in that no two have the same abundance of flowers or the same combinations of species. This is because different kinds of annual wildflowers have different requirements for germination and growth. All need sufficient moisture and warmth, of course, but in varying combinations. Some want cool but not cold temperatures when germinating rains fall; others are more or less indifferent to temperature, as long as it is not too warm, but require abundant rain. Early rains bring forth poppies and lupines, for example, while late rains are congenial to mustards and borages.

In squeezing germination and seed dispersal into a single year, annuals undergo a burst of growth that would not be made possible without abundant—or at least adequate—soil moisture. The need for ample moisture ensures that many annuals will appear only in the wetter years, a rule enforced by strict germination requirements. Otherwise, annuals might germinate in years that were too dry for a complete cycle from seed to seed. Eventually, having used up its existing seeds without producing any replacements, the species would become extinct.

Woody plants are not so much at the mercy of rains. The beginning and the end of their life cycles are typically separated by many years. A seed germinates; ten years later the plant blooms; fifty years after that, it dies. Freed from the pressure to do everything at once, a woody plant need not wait for an exceptionally wet year before it blooms. Many flower every year, in fact, unless there has been unusual drought. In general, the first substantial rain of winter acts as a switch that turns on the processes of flower development. From that point onward, the plant is working toward production of flowers in spring. Nothing shows on the outside of the plant for many months; meanwhile, on the inside, hormones are mobilizing and cells are dividing. Because the pace of flower development, like that of many chemical reactions, depends on warmth, these physiological processes are more rapid during a warm winter and spring, and flowering comes earlier. Cold weather retards flower development. The dependence on temperature means that flowering starts at lower elevations and proceeds upward. February is not too early to see woody plants in bloom in some parts of the Mojave Desert; May is not too late in others.

How to Use This Book

About eight or nine hundred plants in the Mojave Desert could be considered wildflowers. All can be (and have been) described and classified in the pages of a single book. *The Jepson Manual: Higher Plants of California* (University of California Press, 1993) is the most recent example. This authoritative reference also includes all other wildflowers in California as well as many plants that could not be considered wildflowers by any stretch of the imagination—a total of 5,800 species. Because *The Jepson Manual* was written by professional botanists for other professionals, is apt to be most useful to people who are familiar with botanical terminology and who have some training in the use of dichotomous keys. In other words, it is not a book for the casual wildflower lover (although many wildflower lovers have gone on to master the mild difficulties involved and become proficient botanists).

Flowers and Shrubs of the Mojave Desert is meant for anyone who wants to identify and learn about Mojave Desert wildflowers, but it too has its limitations. To devote a full page to every wildflower in the desert would make the book prohibitively expensive. Because some plants have necessarily been omitted, users might well run across flowers that are not depicted in the book. One solution to this problem is to carry several different guides on wildflower forays. The more guides you have, the better your chances of naming what you find. Another pitfall is that some species resemble one another so closely that botanists need dissecting microscopes to tell them apart. When plants look alike, illustrators draw them alike, naturally enough; be aware, however, that these are the very plants that get left out of wildflower books.

The plants in this book are grouped by flower color: green or otherwise inconspicuous, white, yellow, red, and blue. Look for cream-colored flowers in the White section, for orange flowers in Yellow, for shades of pink in Red, and for lavender or purple flowers in Blue.

A common name and a scientific name are given for every plant. Common names are unstandardized. Any single plant might have two or three common names, or, far more likely, none at all. Moreover, people sometimes apply the same common name to several different plants. The solution to this confusion, as the Swedish botanist Carl von Linné (also known as Linnaeus) recognized more than two hundred years ago, is to ensure that each species has one and only one valid name. Because Latin served as a universal language among educated people in his day, he used Latin and Greek roots for plant and animal names. Linnaeus's system of nomenclature gained wide and rapid acceptance and is now used around the world by professionals in all fields of biology.

In accordance with the Linnaean system, a scientific name has three parts: the genus name, the species name, and the authority. The genus is a larger taxonomic unit than the species, just as "desserts" are a larger, more inclusive category than "cakes." A species is basically a single kind or type—the domestic cat is one species, for example, the mountain lion another, and both belong to the genus Felis. The authority is the surname of the botanist who first described the plant as a new species; if other botanists later reassigned the plant to a different genus, their surnames become part of the authority. Surnames are often abbreviated. The scientific names in this book are based for the most part on *The Jepson Manual.*

The only drawback of scientific names is that they intimidate some people unnecessarily. Even among zoologists and botanists, those who have had training in Greek or Latin are in the minority. They do not regard this as a stumbling block, nor should anyone who wants to learn the names of wildflowers. It might help to know that there is much more uniformity in the application of scientific names than in their pronunciation. For one thing, Latin is a dead language, and no one really knows how it sounded when alive. Most biologists pronounce Latin names as their professors did. For another, one's native tongue affects pronunciation; biologists in Mexico and the United States pronounce scientific names differently in accordance with the intonations and accents of Spanish and English. *The Jepson Manual*, which is available at public and university libraries, has a helpful section on pronunciation of scientific names.

Cliff rose blooms in Joshua Tree Forest, Mojave National Preserve, California

Brittlebush in Galena Canyon, Death Valley National Park, California

California poppies and California goldfields, Antelope Valley, California

Desert sand verbena and dune primrose. Borrego Valley in Anza-
Borrego Desert State Park, California

Flowering brittlebush against red sandstone formations, Lake Mead National Recreational Area, Nevada

Pickleweed

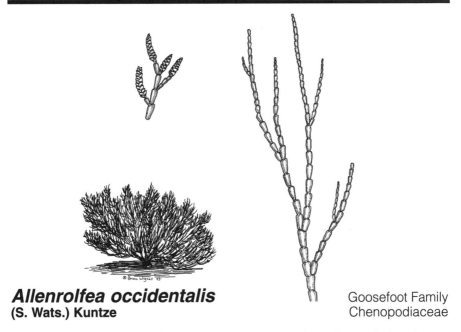

Allenrolfea occidentalis
(S. Wats.) Kuntze

Goosefoot Family
Chenopodiaceae

Pickleweed, a much-branched shrub about three feet tall, has inconspicuous flowers tightly packed together in short cylinders called spikes. Wind pollinates the flowers as it carries pollen from plant to plant. Miniscule leaves may or may not be present. The name comes from the stems, constructed of tiny, pickle-shaped joints stacked one atop another.

Like the pads of prickly pear cactus, pickleweed joints are green and succulent. Green stems enable prickly pear and pickleweed to photosynthesize in the absence of leaves. Succulent stems, however, serve one purpose for prickly pear, another for pickleweed. Succulence helps cacti survive long droughts. Climatic drought is seldom a problem for pickleweed because the plants grow on playas and floodplains where moisture lies close to the surface. On the other hand, playa soils are commonly salty, producing a kind of soil drought. Just as gravity pulls water down an elevational gradient, so differing salt concentrations in the soil pull water along a saline gradient, from regions of low to high salt concentration. Most plants, grown in saline conditions, quickly lose water to the soil and die. The succulent tissues of pickleweed serve as storage depots for salt molecules, making the sap even saltier than the soil and reversing the gradient so that moisture flows from the ground into the plant. Steeped in brine from top to bottom, pickleweed is very much a pickled weed.

The tiny, reddish-brown seeds are produced in great abundance in winter. Native Americans toasted the seeds, then ground them and cooked them into a gruel. Doves, quail, and other seed-eating birds relish the seeds, too.

White bursage

Ambrosia dumosa
(A. Gray) Payne

Sunflower Family
Asteraceae

A small, sturdy shrub as compact as a hassock, white bursage is abundant in the driest parts of western Arizona, southeastern California, and southern Nevada, where it grows on gravelly plains, volcanic malpais, rocky hillslopes, and dunes. Its success is due in part to precise adaptation to aridity. When the soil becomes so dry that photosynthesis is no longer possible, leaves wither and eventually drop off.

White bursage is a common nurse plant; among its dense stems, seedlings hide from hungry rabbits, rodents, and cows, and also escape the worst of summer heat and winter cold. Creosotebush seedlings, for example, seldom colonize open ground; instead, they get started under nurse plants such as white bursage. Although the two species share thousands of square miles of desert, creosotebush does not return the favor; fortunately for white bursage, its seedlings can survive without the benefit of a nurse plant.

Inconspicuous flower heads, comprising a few tiny flowers contained by green bracts, appear early in spring at the stem tips. You can recognize the male, staminate flower heads by their dangling anthers. They are borne above the female, pistillate flower heads, which look like miniature, green burs. Wind blows pollen from plant to plant, fertilizing the pistillate heads, and eventually they mature into hard, spiny burs. Derived from two individual flowers that behave as a unit, the burs cling to fur and clothing, hitching a ride as a means of dispersal.

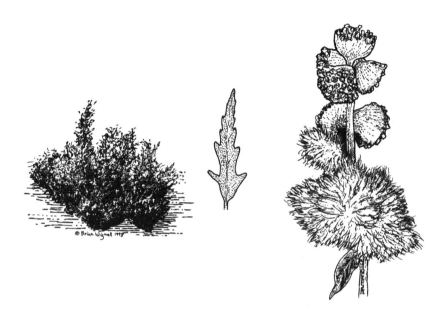

Ambrosia eriocentra
(A. Gray) Payne

Sunflower Family
Asteraceae

About a dozen different bursages have evolved in the deserts of the southwestern United States and northwestern Mexico. Some, like the ubiquitous white bursage, are widely distributed in the Mojave Desert. Most have a more restricted range. Woolly bursage, for example, a shrub three to four feet high, is endemic to the region where California, Nevada, and Arizona meet. From this center of distribution, the species has filtered southeast along the Salt and Gila Rivers, establishing populations all the way to Phoenix, Arizona. Throughout its range, woolly bursage is found in sandy or gravelly washes. As both the common and Latin names imply (*erio* means woolly), most parts of the plant are covered with fine, tangled hairs.

Inconspicuous flowers, grouped in equally inconspicuous flower heads, appear at the stem tips from March through May. They are pollinated as wind blows pollen from the male flower heads on one plant to the female flower heads on another, an inefficient process that requires abundant pollen production for success. Wind pollination is one reason why bursages dominate much of the desert. In years when insects are few or otherwise occupied, bursage can still set a good crop of fruit; meanwhile, creosotebush and other species that require bee pollination can produce little if any seed.

Fourwing saltbush

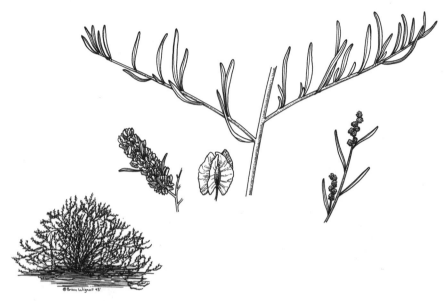

Atriplex canescens
(Pursh) Nutt.

Goosefoot Family
Chenopodiaceae

Fourwing saltbush, a stiffly branched shrub about four or five feet high, gets its name from the winged fruits. Derived from flower bracts, the four wings enclose a single seed. Fourwing saltbush is dioecious, a Latin term meaning "two households" and indicating that the male flowers, which have stamens but not pistils, and the female flowers, which have pistils but not stamens, are borne on separate plants. In human populations, the sex ratio is about fifty percent male, fifty percent female. Fourwing saltbush populations are generally sixty percent female, thirty-six percent male, and four percent undecided. Unlike most plants, fourwing saltbush can change its gender when necessary. Because male plants require less water, females are apt to switch sex during drought. Producing pollen requires less energy than producing fruit, so female plants may also switch sex after a heavy seed-bearing year. As females-turned-males, they accumulate energy reserves for the following year, when they will become females again.

This species is widely distributed in the western United States and grows from sea level to 7,000 feet and from desert to forest. Alkaline plains, rocky slopes, and stable dunes are a few of the many habitats where it thrives. Fourwing saltbush is a good example of ecotypic differentiation—the evolution of different forms to suit specific habitats and climates. Plant breeders have even developed a variety that performs well on the toxic soil of mine wastes.

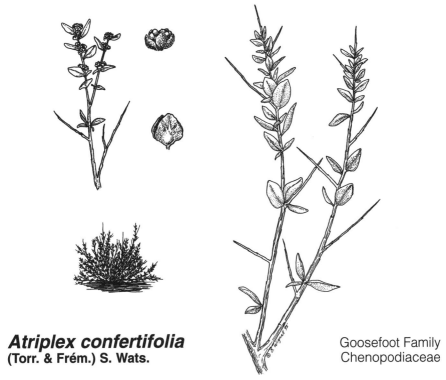

Atriplex confertifolia
(Torr. & Frém.) S. Wats.

Goosefoot Family
Chenopodiaceae

Shadscale, a densely branched shrub one to two feet high, is sometimes called "spiny saltbush" because the woody stem tips become rigid and sharply pointed. The small leaves vary in shape from nearly circular to elliptic or oblong and have smooth margins. Thickly clustered near the stem tips, shadscale fruits consist of a single seed squeezed between two papery bracts. The bracts often turn red or pink as they mature.

Many desert shrubs are drought-deciduous, dropping all their leaves during the summer dry season and remaining dormant until the following spring, but shadscale retains some leaves year-round. Its "semi-evergreen" habit gives shadscale a head start in spring: whereas other shrubs must wait while meristems develop into leaf buds and leaf buds into full-fledged leaves, shadscale can photosynthesize with old leaves while new leaves are under construction.

In the northern part of the Mojave Desert, shadscale can be the dominant plant on silty flats and gravelly plains. It thrives where other warm-desert shrubs cannot—in closed drainage basins where nighttime temperatures often drop below freezing and where the fine-textured and somewhat salty soils are stingy with moisture. This tolerance for cold allows it to grow to elevations of 7,000 feet above sea level.

Desert holly

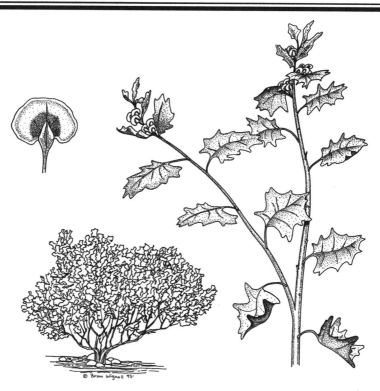

© Brian Wignall '93

Atriplex hymenelytra
(Torr.) S. Wats.

Goosefoot Family
Chenopodiaceae

Desert holly is evergreen in the sense that it retains its jagged leaves year-round, but much of the year those leaves are silver, not green, thanks to abundant silvery scales that cover the leaf blades. In winter and spring, the scales become less prominent as rains fatten the leaves, and the green tissues under the scales peek through. As the soil dries out during the summer and fall, the leaves lose moisture too, becoming shriveled and brittle until you might take them for dead. At the hottest, driest times of year, a number of leaves (but seldom all of them) might drop.

These visible phases go hand in hand with invisible physiological processes. When the leaves are green and succulent, they are very receptive to sunlight, which is of course necessary for photosynthesis. Rapid photosynthesis in winter and spring spurs production of new, leafy shoots and of inconspicuous flowers. When silvery and dry, the leaves reflect much of the incoming sunlight, and photosynthesis drops by fifty percent or more. These and other adaptations enable desert holly to thrive in the hottest, driest part of the Mojave Desert where few woody plants can survive.

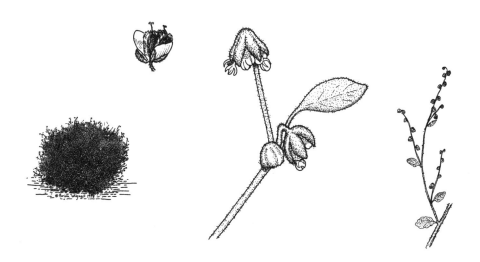

Dicoria canescens
Torr. & Gray

Sunflower Family
Asteraceae

Dune dicoria is a common annual of dunes and sandy flats. Sand dunes are by nature windy places, and like many plants that grow on deep sand, dune dicoria uses the wind for seed dispersal. Each seed has its own sail, a papery cup about twice as long as the seed itself.

Any adaptive modification such as the wing on a seed must arise from some pre-existing structure. In dune dicoria, the sail starts out as one of seven or so inconspicuous greenish bracts that surround a cluster of tiny flowers. As the seeds mature, five or six of the bracts turn dry and brittle, but the other one or two swell as if filling with wind, and eventually they detach, each with a single seed tucked inside. After the seeds mature, the plants die. Sometimes the dried plants turn into tumbleweeds, blowing about the dunes and dispersing any seeds that remain. Dune dicoria seedlings have long, lance-shaped leaves that are very different from the ovate or round leaves of older plants. Either way, the leaves and stems are rough with stiff hairs.

Overall, the plants have a rather weedy look, which is not surprising given that their closest relatives are the roadside ragweeds (*Ambrosia* spp.). "Weedy," used in this sense, is not necessarily a pejorative term. It is true that people are apt to refer to any plant as a weed if it fails to improve human welfare; on the other hand, weediness is a convenient way of referring to a combination of traits including vigorousness, prolific seed production, and readiness to occupy disturbed sites. Weediness in this sense is a lifestyle, and if this lifestyle enables certain plants to colonize, say, a vegetable garden, the gardener might do well to recall who disturbed the soil in the first place.

Boundary mormon tea

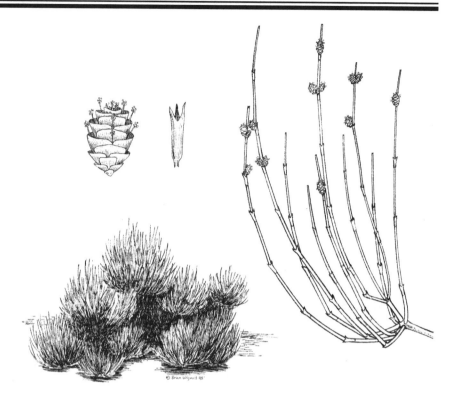

Ephedra nevadensis
S. Wats.

Joint-fir Family
Ephedraceae

Mormon teas are of ancient lineage, having evolved well before flowering plants. Instead of flaunting pretty flowers to attract insect pollinators, mormon teas produce small, papery cones that rely on wind for pollination. The cones consist of overlapping bracts that enfold either stamens (in the case of male plants) or ovules (in the case of female plants).

Boundary mormon tea, a brushy shrub, grows to a height of three or four feet and looks like an unkempt broomhead. The slender stems are pale green at first, turning yellow-green, then gray, in age. The miniscule leaves are produced in pairs on new growth. They eventually split and fall off, leaving their gray bases behind. Lacking leaves much of the year, the plants rely on the green stems for photosynthesis. In years of good winter rains, the plants grow rapidly. In other years they grow little if at all, simply biding their time. Because boundary mormon tea can live well over one hundred years, time is something they have plenty of. This species is common on gravelly slopes and rocky hills.

Western mugwort

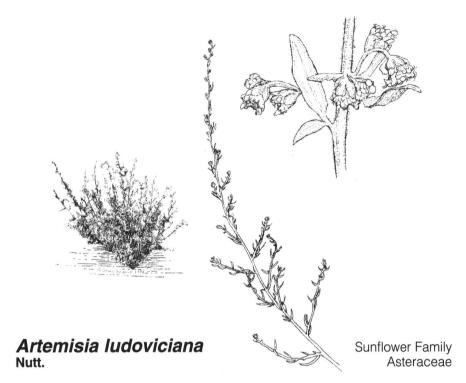

Artemisia ludoviciana
Nutt.

Sunflower Family
Asteraceae

Western mugwort, a perennial herb, is one of the most widely distributed species in the American West, thriving equally well among pines in the mountains and creosotebushes on the plains. In the Mojave Desert, you can find it along dry streambeds or on shaded slopes, often in the shelter of shrubs. A single plant, spreading by underground stems called "rhizomes," can take up a surprising amount of ground.

When crushed, the leaves release a pungent smell reminiscent of its woody relative, big sagebrush. The camphor-like odor might remind some people of home remedies, and indeed western mugwort is highly regarded by *curanderas*, healers familiar with traditional herbal remedies. Essential oils contained in specially modified hairs on the leaves give western mugwort a number of medicinal uses, such as poultices for stomach ache, tea for gastrointestinal disorders, and a hot vapor bath for colds. Camphor in the leaves gives them astringent properties but might also trigger seizures.

Although the blossoms are not showy, western mugwort has a soft beauty of its own. Woolly hairs make the foliage blue-green or bluish-gray when young, almost white in age. The slender leaves can be slightly toothed or deeply cut into jagged lobes. In summer and fall, inconspicuous flower heads are borne on thin stalks at the stem tips.

23

Desert fan palm

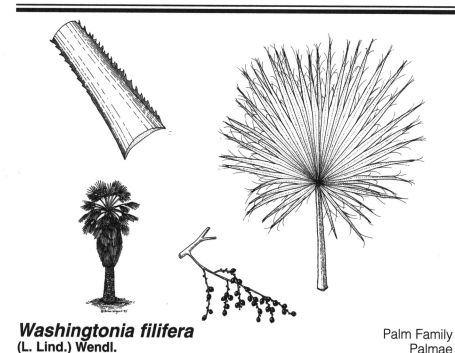

Washingtonia filifera
(L. Lind.) Wendl.

Palm Family
Palmae

Although many kinds of palms are cultivated in the desert cities of Arizona, Nevada, and California, this is the only palm native to the southwestern United States. Fossils show that ten million years ago, the species extended from the Mojave Desert to the Pacific Coast. Geologic and climatic changes eliminated it from much of this area, and today it is found only in the low deserts of western Arizona, Nevada, and southeastern California, typically in steep canyons near small, trickling streams.

The frond of a desert fan palm—actually a single leaf—may reach six feet or more in width. The characteristic accordion pleats give the leaves rigidity, preventing them from collapsing like a flag on a still day. If undisturbed, the leaves accumulate around the trunk as they die, eventually making a shaggy skirt some forty or fifty feet long. Too often, vandals burn the skirts, producing naked, blackened trunks.

Native Americans found many uses for the desert fan palm: they thatched their dwellings with its leaves, wove the leaf fibers into ropes and baskets, preserved the fruits and ground the seeds into meal. Birds and coyotes also eat the fruits, which are wrinkled and dry but nutritious nonetheless. The seeds pass unharmed through the coyote digestive tract, and, as a result, coyotes disperse the species from place to place. Native peoples may well have planted seeds in appropriate locations, thus multiplying the number of groves.

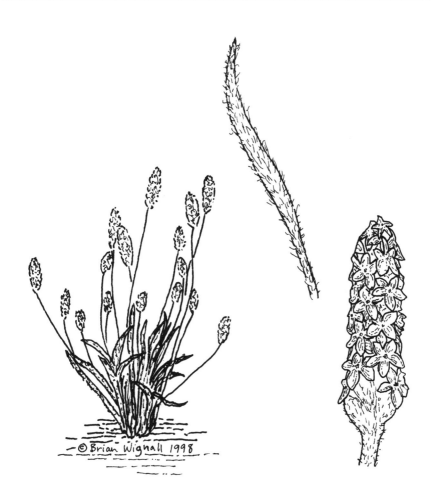

© Brian Wignall 1998

Plantago ovata
Forsskal

Plantain Family
Plantaginaceae

After wet winters, this diminutive annual can be so abundant that it casts a pale green haze over acres of shrubby flats. The tiny, inconspicuous flowers are densely grouped in small egg-shaped heads. Each flower has four papery, translucent petals and four green sepals. Fuzzy with soft white hairs, the narrow, grasslike leaves are clustered at the base of the flowering stalk. There are two reddish-brown seeds per capsule.

Woolly plantain has been used medicinally by Native Americans for various gastrointestinal ailments.

Desert mistletoe

Phoradendron californicum
Nutt.

Mistletoe family
Viscaceae

The genus name *Phoradendron* means "tree thief" in Greek, appropriately enough given that mistletoes are parasitic, taking water and nutrients from other plants. Desert mistletoe can grow on several different trees and shrubs, including catclaw (*Acacia greggii*), mesquite (*Prosopis glandulosa, Prosopis velutina*), and paloverde (*Cercidium floridum*). From a distance, desert mistletoe looks like a bundle of sticks caught in the branches of a tree. Birds spread most mistletoe seeds, eating the small, succulent berries and excreting the seeds. To germinate, the seeds must land on an appropriate host plant. After germination, seedlings penetrate the host with rootlike connections called haustoria.

Desert mistletoe, like any other woody plant in the desert, cannot afford to ignore the scarcity of water in its environment. If its demand for water were too great, the parasite would simply kill its host, thereby ending its own life, as well. Desert mistletoe conserves water by having tiny, scalelike leaves and flowers. Although the flowers are inconspicuous, they are strongly fragrant and attractive to bees. The white or pinkish berries require two years to mature. Phainopeplas, glossy black or gray birds with white wing patches, rely heavily on desert mistletoe fruits.

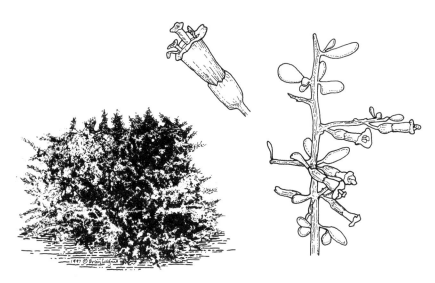

Lycium cooperi
A. Gray

Nightshade Family
Solanaceae

Lycium andersonii
A. Gray

Wolfberries, or box thorns, all look much alike; they have thorny, striated stems, red or orange berries, and, after substantial rains, small, short-lived leaves. Among the common species in the Mojave Desert are Cooper wolfberry and Anderson wolfberry. The Cooper wolfberry can best be told from the others when the yellowish or orangish berries hang from the stems. Each berry is constricted above the middle, and contains several seeds. Anderson wolfberry fruits are bright red spheres containing many seeds. The small, funnel-shaped flowers of these two species are generally white, tinged with lavender. Nectar at the base of the floral tube attracts bees and sometimes hummingbirds.

Spring flowering in these species probably depends on winter rains. If the winter is dry, blooming is sparse, and the berry crop is apt to be poor or non-existent. In good years, heavily bearing plants provide an abundant harvest for birds and rodents. Normally insectivorous birds such as the northern mockingbird feed the berries to their young, enhancing their diets with vitamins and minerals not found in insects. Ground squirrels, clambering into the branches, brave exposure to predators for the sake of the fruits. Native Americans collected and ate the berries; in hard times, they raided woodrat nests in the hope of finding a stash of berries, dried and packed in slabs.

Catclaw

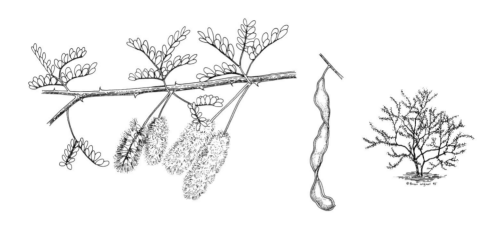

Acacia greggii
A. Gray

Pea Family
Fabaceae

The wide, flat fruits of catclaw are often twisted or curled. They split open to reveal several dark brown seeds shaped like oversized lentils. The seeds are hard and impervious to water. Like those of many legumes, they will not germinate until they have been scarified—nicked with a razor blade, for instance. Through the opening thus made, seeds take up water, swell, and germinate. In nature, where there are no razor blades, the sharp teeth of rodents can do the trick, as can tumbling among rocks in washes. Another means of scarification, perhaps the most common, happens as buried seeds go through cyles of heat and cold, moisture and drought. The seed coat successively expands and contracts and, after a year or two, finally cracks, allowing the embryo to escape from its long confinement.

The creamy flowers, clustered in caterpillar-like spikes, appear in April and May. They are sweet scented and attract a wide variety of bees, hoverflies, wasps, and butterflies. Ants get into the act, too, by visiting the sugar-exuding nectary on the leaf axis. Honeybees make excellent honey from catclaw nectar.

Catclaw is more tolerant of cold weather than most acacias and occurs as far north as southern Nevada and southwestern Utah. Where winters are mild, as in the Mexican states of Sonora and Chihuahua, catclaw can be a tree up to twenty feet in height. Over much of its range, however, it is a spreading shrub not much more than five or six feet tall. The shrubs are found most often along sandy washes. They can live for at least two hundred years. The distinctive spines, shaped like a cat's claw, give this species its common name.

Rush milkweed

© Brian Wignall 93'

Asclepias subulata
Decne.

Milkweed Family
Asclepiadaceae

When rush milkweed blooms in spring, you can sometimes hear the plants before you see them, so dense is the population of buzzing insect visitors. A variety of wasps, bees, and hoverflies gather to sip nectar from the flowers, and you are almost assured of seeing a tarantula hawk, a large, orange-bodied wasp with blue-black wings, among them.

Milkweed pollen is packaged in pollinia, which resemble tiny wishbones. Pollinia clip onto the legs of insect visitors, then unclip when inserted into another milkweed flower. Large insects, like the tarantula hawk, make the best milkweed pollinators.

The clumped, rushlike plants are three to four feet high and can be found at roadsides and in washes.

Desert milkweed

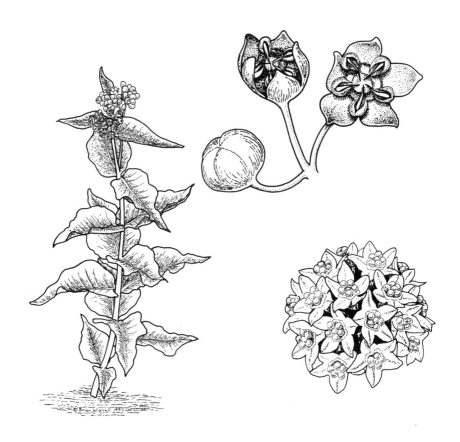

Asclepias erosa
Torrey

Milkweed Family
Asclepiadaceae

This perennial herb is a desert version of *Asclepias speciosa*, or showy milkweed, a common weed in pastures and at roadsides in the moister parts of the western United States and Canada. Both have large leaves, but those of desert milkweed are leathery instead of soft, and the flowers are ivory colored instead of pink.

Desert milkweed stems grow in clumps up to five feet high. Flower heads the size of baseballs are borne on the upper part of the stem. The plants are most often found in washes and at roadsides, where runoff after rains gives them extra moisture.

Baccharis salicifolia
(Ruiz & Pav.) Pers.

Sunflower Family
Asteraceae

Ranging as far south as Guatemala and Honduras, this tall, leafy shrub is accustomed to torrid temperatures and does not mind heat as long as the roots have access to water. In the Southwest, seep willows form graceful thickets along rivers, streambanks, and irrigation canals. Even intermittent streams provide suitable habitat as long as water is available beneath the surface. Despite its willowlike leaves and its streambed habitat, seep willow is not a willow at all but a member of the large and diverse Sunflower Family.

When they bloom in summer and fall, the miniscule flowers attract an astounding variety of insects. The flowers are arranged in flat-topped clusters that make good landing platforms for butterflies, bees, wasps, and hover-flies. The long, narrow leaves are evergreen or nearly so; a glistening resin on the leaf blades probably serves the dual functions of deterring herbivores and slowing water loss.

Phytochemists have recently discovered that the foliage contains several compounds that inhibit bacterial activity. Not surprisingly, seep willow has been known as a medicinal plant since the time of the Aztecs, and probably long before. It has been used to reduce swelling and to treat wounds and bruises.

Cliff rose

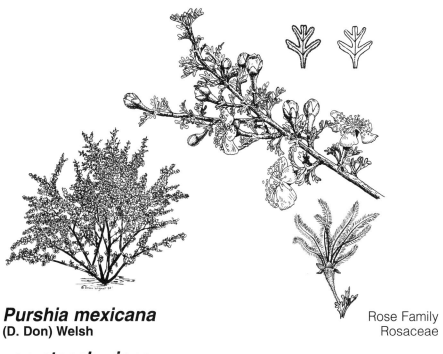

Purshia mexicana
(D. Don) Welsh

Rose Family
Rosaceae

var. stansburiana
(Torr.) Welsh

Like many desert shrubs, cliff rose requires a substantial rain to trigger flowering. Either winter or summer rains will do; in the Mojave Desert, where summer storms are uncommon, cliff rose blooms most reliably in spring. The large white flowers are sweetly fragrant; sometimes you can smell them from your car as you drive by. Because they are dish-shaped and open, cliff rose blossoms allow access to a wide variety of insect visitors. In scrambling across the stamens, insects inadvertently dust themselves with pollen, which they carry to the pistil of the next flower they visit.

Each fertilized pistil eventually produces a single-seeded fruit called an achene. A pistil has three parts: the ovary, which is where seeds develop; the stigma, a kind of sticky platform that receives the pollen; and the style, a tube that connects stigma and ovary. After cliff rose ovaries are fertilized, the style becomes a plume that catches in the wind and disperses the seed. A single flower may produce as many as ten plumed achenes.

Cliff rose is found on rocky slopes where, especially in winter when little else is available, deer browse the foliage despite its bitter taste and acrid smell. Like many unpleasant-tasting plants, cliff rose has a number of medicinal uses, and another common name is quinine bush.

Ragged rock flower

© Brian Wignall 93'

Crossosoma bigelovii
S. Wats.

Crossosoma Family
Crossosomataceae

Ragged rock flower, or desert mock-orange as it is sometimes called, is a woody plant seldom more than three or four feet in height. Both names are appropriate: the shrubs often grow from cracks in cliffs, and the sweet and spicy scent of the white flowers is somewhat reminiscent of citrus blossoms. Blooming as early as February, ragged rock flower is a harbinger of spring in the canyons of Mojave Desert mountain ranges.

The seed capsules—more properly called follicles—develop in the center of the blossoms. Each follicle contains several seeds, and each seed is wrapped in a fleshy, fringed appendage called an aril. The genus name *Crossosoma* means "fringed body," a reference to the aril. The purpose of the aril is not known, but it probably involves seed dispersal. The arils of certain violets, for instance, are rich in oils. Ants, which love oil-rich foods, carry the seeds to their nests, where they detach the arils and throw away the seeds. Cast-off seeds sometimes land in spots that are suitable for germination and establishment. Perhaps this is how ragged rock flower seeds are dispersed.

California buckwheat

Eriogonum fasciculatum
Benth.

Buckwheat Family
Polygonaceae

This three-foot-high shrub is especially handsome in bloom. The lacy clusters of tiny white flowers, borne on long, leafless stalks, might remind you of yarrow (*Achillea millefolium*) or Queen Anne's lace (*Daucus carota*), but the three are not even remotely related. They resemble one another because they have the same type of inflorescence, an umbel or corymb in which small flowers are arranged in flat-topped bunches. This arrangement facilitates pollination by small nectar-feeding insects. By offering only a tiny amount of nectar in an individual blossom, the plant encourages the insect—often a bee or hoverfly—to seek out other, nearby blossoms. Crawling and scrambling across one flower cluster after another, insects distribute pollen from plant to plant.

Found on rocky slopes in desertscrub and chaparral, wild buckwheat blooms more or less continuously from March until June. Even after the flowers have withered, the rust-colored inflorescences are conspicuous for several months. By virtue of their small size, leathery texture, and inrolled margins, the evergreen leaves resist drought and frost.

It is said that sick headaches (especially hangovers) sometimes respond to hot tea made from wild buckwheat. Native Americans used buckwheat flower tea to ease the aches and pains of advanced pregnancy. The seeds were an important food source for many tribes.

Apache plume

Fallugia paradoxa
(Don) Endl.

Rose Family
Rosaceae

Whether in flower or in fruit, Apache plume catches the eye. The five-petaled flowers are rather large, often more than an inch in diameter. After good winter rains, they blanket the plants with white. The numerous pistils in the center of the blossoms ripen into clusters of delicate plumes that look like feather dusters or sea anemones. Fine, silky hairs make the plumes buoyant enough to disperse in the wind. The plants tend to bear many seeds one year, few seeds the next.

At low elevations, Apache plume is most common in washes and along roadsides, habitats in which extra runoff compensates for the paucity of rainfall. At somewhat higher elevations, the five-foot-tall shrubs thrive on rocky slopes, as well.

At first glance, Apache plume resembles cliff rose, another shrub with shreddy bark, white flowers, and plumed seeds. Apache plume, however, is a spreading shrub, whereas cliff rose is a small, gnarled tree. Cliff rose flowers are smaller (about one-half inch in diameter) and creamy rather than paper white. Each Apache plume flower produces many pinkish plumes, whereas each cliff rose flower produces about ten tawny ones.

35

Honey mesquite

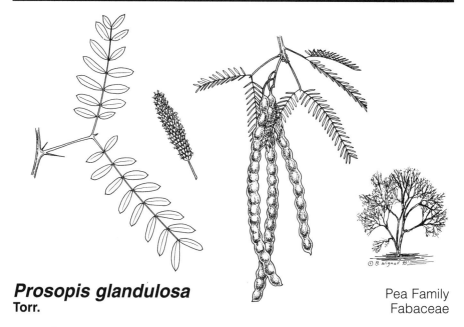

Prosopis glandulosa
Torr.

Pea Family
Fabaceae

var. torreyana
(L. Benson) M. C. Johnst.

Honey mesquite is a shoulder-high shrub where it grows on plains and dunes or, where it grows in major washes and along rivers, a tree as tall as a two-story house. The tiny, creamy or yellowish flowers are densely clustered in cylindrical spikes. Only a few flowers in each spike ripen into six-inch-long, straw-colored pods. Pods contain about eight or ten seeds that are separated from one another by spongy partitions.

Wherever honey mesquite grew, native peoples relied on it heavily. They used every part of the plant, from the sugar-rich pods to the fibrous roots. Typically, the pods were gathered when dry, then toasted. The toasted pods were pounded into a fine-textured flour that was baked into rolls and cakes.

The hard, water-resistant wood not only provided fuel and building materials, it was also fashioned into many useful objects such as bowls, planting sticks, awls, pestles, and cradles. The roots were separated into fibers, then twisted into cordage. The leaves, steeped as a tea, made medicine for treating sore eyes and stomach disorders. Even the black pitch that oozes out of the trunks found its uses as medicinal tea, hair dye, and pottery paint.

Naturally, wildlife make heavy use of honey mesquite, too. Quail eat the flower buds, and innumerable bees and wasps come to the flowers for nectar and pollen. Giant mesquite bugs suck sap from the green pods, and cottontails, ground squirrels, and coyotes eat the ripe pods.

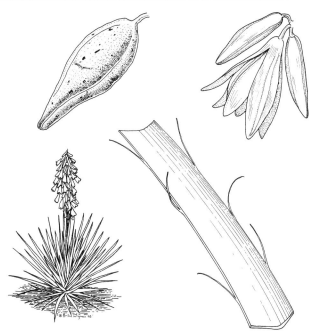

Yucca baccata
Torr.

Agave Family
Agavaceae

The leaves of this yucca can be quite variable—curved or straight, bluish-green or yellowish-green, clustered in a single clump or in colonies. Unlike the Joshua tree and certain other yuccas, the plants do not have a trunk. The fruits are sturdy, green capsules plump with succulent flesh that is relished by a variety of mammals, including Homo sapiens. Most yucca fruits split open when ripe, spilling the seeds to the ground. Banana yucca fruits never split, so the seeds never fall out. Instead, the plants rely on packrats and rabbits to spread the seeds by consuming the fruits. Several million years ago, large mammals like the giant ground sloth, which is now extinct, may have eaten the fruits and dispersed the seeds.

Banana yucca blooms from April to June. During its lifetime, a plant will flower many times, unlike the agaves, or century plants, which flower once, then die. Flowering and fruiting require a considerable expenditure of stored sugars, and after a banana yucca blooms, it must recuperate for several years before it can flower again. Depending on how wet the winter has been, many plants in a population might flower in a given spring, or only a few.

Banana yucca can reach six feet in height, but more often grows to three or four feet. It can be distinguished from Mojave yucca and Joshua tree by the absence of a trunk and by the fleshy fruits.

Joshua tree

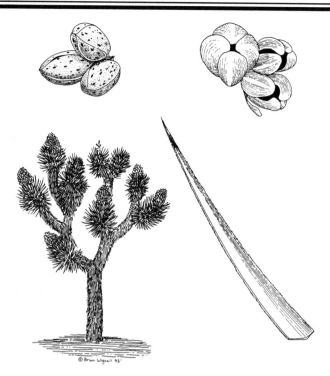

© Brian Wignall 93

Yucca brevifolia
Engelm.

Agave Family
Agavaceae

Early Mormon settlers called this the Joshua tree because the plants seem to lift their arms in supplication like the Biblical prophet Joshua. The trees are patriarchal in age as well as name and probably live for about two hundred years.

Frequently the largest plants by far in the landscape, Joshua trees reach thirty (rarely fifty) feet in height and may spread to twenty feet in diameter. Stiff, green leaves make a spiky head at the end of every branch. Flower stalks bearing dense clusters of white, bell-shaped flowers appear at or near the stem tips in late spring; the flower clusters barely extend beyond the subtending leaves.

The thatch of dead leaves on the lower branches and trunk provides cover for a variety of animals, among them the night lizard, a shy nocturnal lizard that hunts among fallen branches for termites, crickets, and moths. As many as twenty-five different species of birds are associated in one way or another with Joshua trees. Scott's orioles hang their nests from the short, stiff leaves. Northern flickers excavate nest holes in the trunks; later on, other birds occupy the holes.

Yucca schidigera
Roezl ex Ort.

Agave Family
Agavaceae

Reaching a height of three to twelve feet, Mojave yucca has swordlike, yellow-green leaves atop a sturdy trunk that is abundantly cloaked with dead, downward-pointing leaves. The large flowers, which appear in spring, are cream-colored, sometimes tinged with purple. They are borne in loose clusters on short flower stalks.

Like other yuccas, Mojave yucca is pollinated exclusively by female moths in the genus *Tegeticula*. After she mates, the female moth gathers a ball of pollen from the anthers of a yucca flower, then flies to a different yucca plant, where she lays her eggs on the small, green ovary inside a flower. Next she rubs the ball of pollen into the stigmas that sit atop the ovary. As the seeds inside the ovary develop, the moth eggs hatch into tiny caterpillars that eat them. Both the moth and the yucca gain by this arrangement. The flowers are ensured of pollination, and the caterpillars are guaranteed a steady supply of food. Since the caterpillars eat only a fraction of the seeds inside a capsule, plenty of seeds are left for dispersal in late summer.

Desert sumac

Rhus trilobata
Torr. & A. Gray

Cashew Family
Anacardiaceae

Desert sumac, a rounded shrub up to five feet in height, can be found on shaded slopes and in canyon bottoms. The plants start to bloom in spring before the leaves appear. The glossy, green leaves are three-parted and scalloped, but unlike the three-parted leaves of poison ivy, they rarely cause severe dermatitis. The inconspicuous flowers, borne in stalked clusters near the stem tips, are whitish or yellowish. The single-seeded, red or vermilion fruits are covered with sticky hairs. They ripen in summer and are quickly stripped from the plants by birds and ground squirrels. Another common name for this species is lemonadeberry—it is said that a refreshing drink can be made by soaking the fruits (either fresh or dried) in water.

Native Americans knew a number of uses for desert sumac. They discovered that the fruits could be used as a mordant in dyes as well as a flavoring in water. They noticed that the young shoots are long, straight, and supple, making them ideal for basketry when fresh and for arrow shafts when dried. Fire stimulates production of new growth, and in some areas Native Americans might have managed local populations of desert sumac by setting the plants on fire. Contemporary herbalists incorporate the dried and powdered leaves into salves for treating mouth sores and for use as a nasal spray.

Amsonia

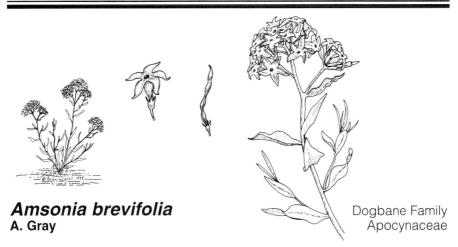

Amsonia brevifolia
A. Gray

Dogbane Family
Apocynaceae

Amsonia, a perennial herb with many leafy stems about ten to fifteen inches long, is locally common in sandy washes of desert plains and mountain canyons. The tubular, five-lobed flowers are white or pale blue and appear in spring at the stem tips. When broken, the stems and leaves exude milky sap. The long, spindle-shaped fruits are constricted between the seeds.

Amsonia has two forms: one with bright green, glabrous leaves, another with gray-hairy leaves. For many years, botanists considered them to be two different species, *Amsonia brevifolia* A. Gray (the green-leaved form) and *Amsonia tomentosa* (the gray-leaved form). When someone finally grew both forms from seeds of a single plant, it was clear that only one species was involved. Hairiness is probably a simple, genetically recessive trait. If both parents have hairy leaves, so will their offspring. Similarly, two green-leaved parents will have green-leaved progeny. But if one parent has hairy leaves and the other has green leaves, the offspring will have green leaves because hairiness (like blue eyes and red hair) is a recessive trait.

When two different scientific names have been applied to the same species, the rules of botanical nomenclature state that the first one to be validly published has priority. Thus the green-leaved form must be called *Amsonia tomentosa*, or woolly amsonia, despite its lack of wool, and the name *Amsonia brevifolia*, which means short-leaved amsonia and applies equally well to both forms, is firmly set aside.

No medicinal uses have been reported for this plant, nor does it have a widely accepted common name. These two characteristics—namelessness and uselessness—are frequent companions because the plants that acquire common names are typically those that have particular value to their namers. Although humans do not use amsonia, moths visit the flowers for nectar and milkweed bugs feed on the sap of the green pods and seeds. Usefulness depends on who you are and what you need.

41

Trailing milkweed

Sarcostemma hirtellum
(A. Gray) R. Holm

Milkweed Family
Asclepiadaceae

A spring-flowering vine with twining stems, trailing milkweed often grows in washes or ditches where it clambers up fences and shrubs. The stems die back to the ground annually; new growth sprouts from the perennial root. Like almost all members of the Milkweed Family, trailing milkweed drips milky sap when cut or broken. The flowers, which smell strongly of onions, are greenish-white, and the foliage is gray-green, traits that help to distinguish this species from the closely related *Sarcostemma cynanchoides* Decne., which has green foliage and pink or purple flowers. Both have narrow or lance-shaped leaves borne in pairs on the slender stems. Upon ripening, the spindle-shaped pods split on one side, releasing flat seeds tufted with silky, one-inch-long hairs that catch in the wind.

The flowers attract butterflies and wasps, especially in a dry spring when little else is in bloom.

Desert star

Monoptilon bellioides
(A. Gray) H. M. Hall

Sunflower Family
Asteraceae

A delicate annual that branches from the base, desert star has one or two flower heads per stem tip. Disk flowers are yellow, ray flowers white, pink or lavender. The small, narrow leaves are clustered around the flower heads and at the base of the plant.

Desert star can be abundant in sandy areas after good winter rains. When the winter has been on the dry side, desert star still makes an appearance, even if only as a single flower head on a much abbreviated stem.

Desert star also grows on desert pavements—not an easy habitat. The soil is somewhat water-repellent and desert pavement often contains more sodium than most plants can tolerate. Desert star manages to thrive under these daunting conditions.

Gravel ghost

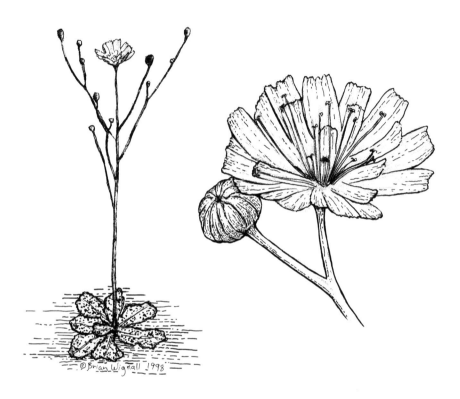

Atrichoseris platyphylla
A. Gray

Sunflower Family
Asteraceae

The white flower heads of gravel ghost sometimes seem to float ghost-like a foot or two above the ground although they are in fact attached to slender, leafless stems. Another common name is parachute plant, also a reference to the apparent weightlessness of the flowers.

Gravel ghost is a member of the family Asteraceae, the Sunflower Family, and of subfamily Liguliflorae. All members of this subfamily have milky sap and heads composed entirely of ray flowers. Gravel ghost is occasional to common on desert pavement and gravelly flats and in sandy washes.

White tackstem

Calycoseris wrightii
A. Gray

Sunflower Family
Asteraceae

Given the propensity of desert plants to arm themselves with spines, thorns, and other painful protrusions, you might expect something fairly horrific from a plant named "tackstem." Fortunately, the tacks referred to are not thumb tacks or carpet tacks, but mildly glutinous hairs shaped like dressmaker's pins. Only the upper part of the stem has tack-shaped glands; the lower part is smooth.

The flower heads of white tackstem are almost two inches in diameter and are borne on stems that look too slender for the weight they must support. The underside of the ray flowers is often dotted or streaked with rose or purple. A closely related species, yellow tackstem (*Calycoseris parryi* A. Gray), has yellow rays instead of white.

Pebble pincushion

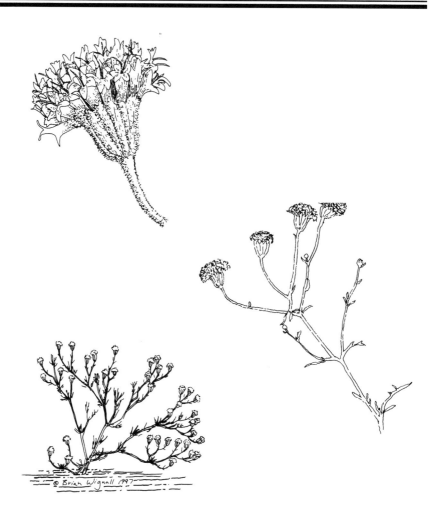

Chaenactis carphoclinia
A. Gray

Sunflower Family
Asteraceae

Pebble pincushion, a delicate annual wildflower with deeply divided leaves, has white or pinkish flowers crowded into heads. If the heads resemble pincushions, then the stamens poking out of the flowers must represent the pins. Erect bracts called "phyllaries" surround the flowers; the phyllaries of a pebble pincushion head are sharply pointed and reddish in color. Tiny, curly hairs make the leaves and stems look white.

46

Desert pincushion

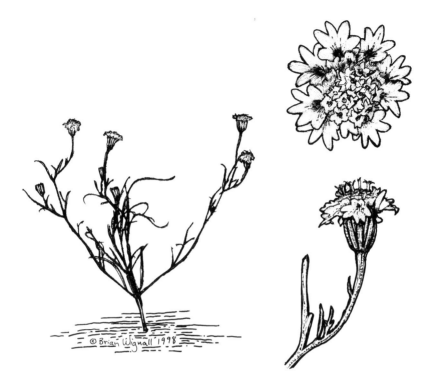

© Brian Wignall 1998

Chaenactis fremontii
A. Gray

Sunflower Family
Asteraceae

Desert pincushion looks much like pebble pincushion, having white (sometimes pinkish) flowers crowded in heads, sharp-pointed phyllaries, and erect, branching stems, but the foliage generally lacks hairs, and the plants are more robust. Leaf margins may be smooth or deeply lobed; the leaves tend to cluster near the base of the plant and often wither before the flowers open. Desert pincushion can be common on gravelly or sandy flats, often growing with creosote bush.

All the flowers in a head are disk flowers, but the outermost flowers are distinctly larger than those in the center. Millions of years of evolution were required for the Sunflower Family to attain the marked reduction and crowding of flowers that is its signal characteristic. In enlarging some of its flowers, desert pincushion has headed in the opposite direction. Larger flowers often contain more pollen or nectar than smaller flowers and might be more appealing to pollinators for that reason. Perhaps the enlarged, ray-like flowers of desert pincushion promise a generous reward to flower visitors.

New Mexico thistle

© Brian Wignall 1993

Cirsium neomexicanum
A. Gray

Sunflower Family
Asteraceae

In Arizona, this species most often has lavender flowers, rarely white, but in the Mojave Desert, white is the common color, although occasional plants have lavender or pale pink flowers. The flowers are aggregated in large heads up to the size of baseballs. A variety of insects visit the flowers during the spring blooming period, among them bumblebees, carpenter bees, honey bees, and pipevine swallowtail butterflies.

In late spring you might see a goldfinch perched on a fruiting head, tugging one achene at a time from its container and plucking off the pappus. The pappus drifts away, a parachute without a jumper, while the goldfinch husks the achene and eats the seed inside.

© Brian Wignall 1998

Layia glandulosa
(Hook.) Hook. & Arn.

Sunflower Family
Asteraceae

The common name "tidy tips" more properly belongs to a closely related species that has yellow rays tipped with white. The rays of *Layia glandulosa* are entirely white, making it an untipped tidy tips. This lovely annual can be found on open slopes and plains, often in sandy soils. Each flower head comprises yellow disk flowers surrounded by white ray flowers. In the desert, white tidy tips can be distinguished from look-alikes by the pinlike glands on the stems and by the rose-purple color of the fading rays.

Rock daisy

Peralty emoryi
Torr.

Sunflower Family
Asteraceae

A perky annual that can be one inch or three feet in height, depending on how much water it gets, rock daisy grows on rocky slopes, in cliff crevices, and along sandy washes. Appearing as early as February, the dime-sized flower heads have yellow disk flowers in the center and white ray flowers around the perimeter. Occasional plants have disk flowers only. The bright green leaves, more or less ovate in shape, have lobed margins, and the lobes themselves are irregularly toothed. Glandular hairs can make the foliage feel clammy to the touch. Sometimes spinelike hairs are present, too.

The scientific name of rock daisy commemorates William H. Emory, commissioner of the team that surveyed the United States and Mexico boundary just after the war between those two countries. Although primarily a military man, Emory took a lively interest in the natural history of the border states, and he encouraged and supported the various botanists under his command. Emory's contribution to their efforts is recognized and remembered in *Peralty emoryi* and many other plants of the border states.

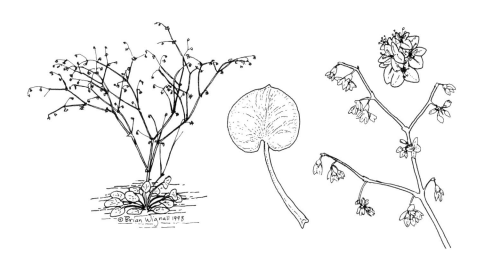

Eriogonum deflexum
Torr.

Buckwheat Family
Polygnaceae

There are 250 species of wild buckwheat, plants in the genus *Eriogonum,* in North America. In California, *Eriogonum* is represented by more species than any other genus, and a fair percentage of them can be found in the Mojave Desert. One of those, a common wildflower of roadsides and sandy or gravelly washes, is skeleton weed, sometimes called flat-topped buckwheat. It belongs to a group characterized by an annual habit and flower clusters that are turned downward or borne on stalks. Like many other native plants with "weed" in their names, skeleton weed is notable for its ability to grow on sites that are impoverished in one way or another—little soil, little (if any) nitrogen, scant water. This kind of weedy toughness enables skeleton weed to be among the first plants to colonize disturbed sites, starting the long process of restoring natural desert.

Round or kidney-shaped in outline, the leaves form a rosette at the base of the stem. They are densely woolly beneath and grayish-green above. The flowering stalk is leafless and stiffly branched. At widely spaced intervals on the uppermost stems are down-turned, bell-shaped flower clusters. Individual flowers are tiny. Each has three white or pinkish sepals and three white or pinkish petals. Sepals and petals in the genus *Eriogonum* are sometimes called "tepals," indicating that sepals and petals are virtually identical.

Skeleton weed flowers during warm weather. Bees are frequent flower visitors. After the plants die, they turn rust-colored and can remain standing for many months.

Desert chicory

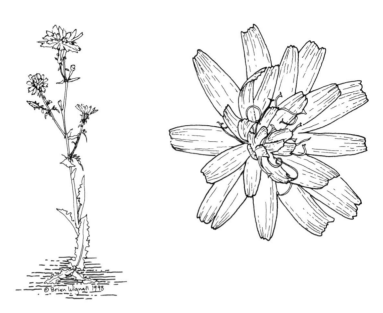

© Brian Wignall 1998

Rafinesquia neomexicana
Nutt.

Sunflower Family
Asteraceae

An attractive annual with milky sap in the stems and leaves, desert chicory sometimes sprawls on the lowermost branches of nearby shrubs. The large, white flower heads are borne singly at the stem tips. All the flowers are strap-shaped, five-toothed rays. Leaves are deeply lobed or irregularly toothed, sometimes both. The ripe fruits, called achenes, are dry and single-seeded. Each achene tapers into a slender beak to which a tuft of silky, white bristles is attached. When the plants are in fruit, the interlocking bristles of adjacent achenes form a soft, white globe.

The genus name commemorates Constantine Rafinesque, an eccentric naturalist who was born in Turkey and raised in France. He travelled extensively in the United States in the early nineteenth century, collecting bats, snakes, birds, fish, plants, and fossils. His passion for natural history was unbounded. Staying overnight with the ornithologist John James Audubon, Rafinesque awoke the household with the uproar he made as he chased an undescribed species of bat around his room, swatting at it with Audubon's priceless Cremorna violin.

Desert chicory usually grows in canyon bottoms and on rocky slopes, often in the shade of larger plants. It can be distinguished from other white-flowered annuals in this family by the large heads, the hairless foliage, and the rose-purple veins on the undersides of the rays.

Popcorn flower

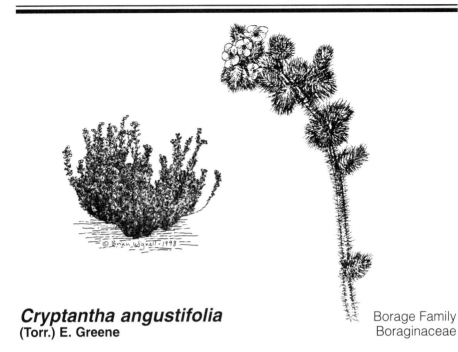

Cryptantha angustifolia
(Torr.) E. Greene

Borage Family
Boraginaceae

A spring-blooming annual common in sandy washes and on gravelly flats, this bristly little plant has the coiled flower stalked typical of the Borage Family. The diminutive white flower is a short, five-lobed tube. The fruit comprises three or four pyramidal nutlets joined to a common axis. At maturity, one nutlet is distinctly larger than the others. Leaves are much longer than wide, as suggested by the species name *angustifolia*, which means narrow-leaved. The plants can produce many stems from the base or only a few, depending on how much rain they have received.

The opening of the flower is so tiny that you cannot even see the stamens and pistil inside the tube, so tiny, in fact, that most insects cannot get access to the pollen. An exception is the small solitary bee *Proteriades*, which has special curling bristles on its mouthparts to extract *Cryptantha* pollen without entering the flower. These bees might carry some pollen from plant to plant, thus fertilizing the ovaries; for the most part, however, the flowers probably pollinate themselves without benefit of insect intermediaries.

The name "popcorn flower" is that rare thing—a genuine common name—and should be treasured even though it refers to many species of *Cryptantha* rather than just one. *Cryptantha angustifolia* is sometimes called narrowleaf cryptantha, which is merely a translation of the scientific name and only a partial translation, at that. *Cryptantha* is Greek for "hidden flowers," so the fully translated name would be "narrowleaf hidden flowers," hardly an improvement over popcorn flower.

Spectacle pod

© Brian Wignall 1997

Dithyrea californica
Harv.

Mustard Family
Brassicaceae

Named for the bilobed fruit that looks like a pair of eyeglasses, specta-cle pod is a common spring-flowering annual on dunes and sandy flats. The sweetly scented flowers have four white or lavender petals and four green sepals. Stem leaves, when present, are oblong to ovate in shape and up to two inches long. Basal leaves can be as much as six inches in length and are widest above the middle. The most distinctive feature are the spectacle-like fruits.

Like many spring wildflowers of the Mojave Desert, spectacle pod is a winter annual. To germinate, the seeds require cool (but not cold) soils and at least an inch of rain, a combination of circumstances that is most likely to happen in autumn or early winter.

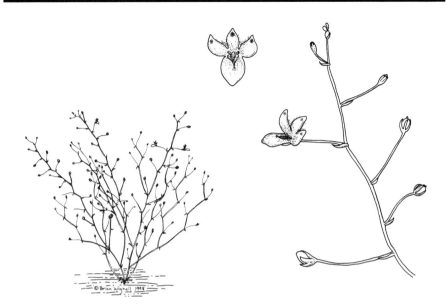

Nemacladus glanduliferus
Jepson

Bellflower Family
Campanulaceae

Its stems are so fine and its flowers so small that you can look through a threadplant and never see it. What is apt to catch your eye is the basal rosette of small leaves. More or less elliptic in shape, the leaves are toothed or deeply lobed and grayish green in color. Rising from the rosette are several slender, zigzag stems. Miniscule white flowers are borne at the tips of stemlets that are even more slender than the main stems. Appearing in spring, the delicate, orchidlike flowers repay examination under a magnifying lens.

Threadplant is an annual that can be common on roadsides and gravelly flats and in sandy washes. The Bellflower Family, to which threadplant and its twelve sibling species belong, is unusually well represented in California and includes thirteen species in the genus *Downingia* and one species each in the genera *Heterocodon* and *Legenere*. Most species in these three genera are annuals that grow only in vernal pools and other wet habitats. In contrast, the threadplants are annuals that are adapted to dry, rather sterile or barren sites—deserts, of course, and also burned areas in chaparral and soils derived from serpentine. What these various genera have in common is that they specialize in "difficult" habitats. Vernal pools dry up when summer arrives, as does the desert. By existing as flowering plants during the most favorable season and as seeds at other times of year, threadplant and its relatives make the best of their uneven environment.

Dodder

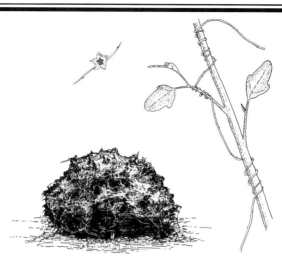

Cuscuta denticulata
Engelm.

Dodder Family
Cuscutaceae

The individual species of dodder can be difficult to tell apart, but the genus is easily recognized by the twining, threadlike stems, either yellow or orange, that wrap themselves around the stems of other plants. This is not a friendly embrace: dodders are parasites. Lacking chlorophyll, they cannot photosynthesize and must extract the sugars they need for growth from their hosts; lacking roots, they get the water they need from the same source. Most species of dodder are rather catholic in their tastes and can grow on a number of different species. *Cuscuta denticulata*, for example, can be found on creosotebush, tamarisk, desert tobacco, and spurge, among others. The small, white flowers of *Cuscuta denticulata* are bell-shaped and clustered in twos and threes.

California dodder, *Cuscuta californica* Hook. & Arn., grows outside the desert but is probably familiar to many travelers as an orange, webby mass draped across certain shrubs along California roadsides and highways.

The parasitic habit is apt to rouse indignation in human hearts. Is not life in the desert hard enough without the added burden of parasitism? The answer might not be as clear-cut as we suppose. In fact, finding an answer would involve asking and answering many other questions first. For example, how do seeds locate an appropriate host, and how many seeds are wasted in the process? What conditions are required for germination? Is there a preference for healthy hosts, or does dodder perform best on hosts that are already stressed in some way? How often (if ever) does dodder actually kill its host? Exploring these and other possibilities, we might discover that dodder has problems of its own. We might even find room in our hearts for something besides indignation.

Eucnide urens
(Gray) Parry

Loasa Family
Loasaceae

Rock nettles often grow on cliffs, making a cascade of creamy flowers and foliage. They also form large, spreading mounds on rocky slopes. The flowers have five petals that overlap at the edges, making a funnel-shaped blossom as much as two inches in length. Except for the petals, all parts of the plant, including the large, coarsely toothed leaves, bristle with two types of hairs. Either type is quite capable of piercing tender skin and inflicting pain. The long, slender hairs can sting, and the shorter, barbed hairs break off in tender skin. Where rock nettles grow close to cave entrances, bats have reportedly impaled themselves on the hairs.

The stinging hairs of rock nettle have not been specifically investigated; however, they might work much like those of the true nettles in the genus *Urtica* (Nettle Family or Uticaceae). The stinging hairs of true nettles work like hypodermic syringes. Each hair is actually a needle-sharp tube arising from a sac that contains histamines and other irritating chemicals. A hand brushing against the hairs breaks off the needle tips, and the pressure on the sacs forces irritants up the tube and into the hand.

Wishbone bush

Mirabilis bigelovii
Gray

Four O'Clock Family
Nyctaginaceae

Wishbone bush is a sprawling perennial of rocky slopes. It blooms in spring and sometimes again in fall. Borne in pairs, the triangular or heart-shaped leaves are rather large and soft for the desert, so the plants generally do best when growing in the shade of shrubs or overhanging boulders. Even then, wishbone bush is apt to wilt on hot days and to lose its leaves during long dry spells. Stalked glands, barely visible to the naked eye, make the leaves and stems feel tacky or even clammy to the touch. The white or pale pink flowers open late in the afternoon.

Flowers typically comprise a certain number of petals set inside a certain number of sepals. The petals, taken collectively, are the corolla; similarly, the sepals are the calyx. We think of petals as being brightly colored, sepals as being green. Wishbone bush, along with several other members of the Four O'Clock Family, flouts this convention. Because the funnel-shaped flowers of wishbone bush are actually fused sepals, each flower is a calyx. Despite appearances to the contrary, wishbone bush has no petals and therefore no corolla.

Camissonia boothii
(Douglas) Raven

ssp. *condensata*
(Munz) Raven

Evening Primrose Family
Onagraceae

The small, four-petaled flowers of this spring-blooming annual open at dusk and wilt the next morning. Their white color and delicate fragrance attract moths as pollinators. Each flower sits atop a long, slender ovary that is in turn attached to the shreddy stem. After pollination, the ovaries ripen into seed pods that neither fall nor split open for some time. The dry pods on the sturdy stems look like the bristles of a bottle brush, thus the common name. As the tips of the seed pods finally pull apart, some seeds drop to the ground near the parent plant. Eventually, the dead stems break free of the root and tumble across the ground, scattering seeds as they go. This apparently haphazard means of dispersal works well in the sandy, windy habitats where woody bottle washer usually grows.

Brown-eyed evening primrose

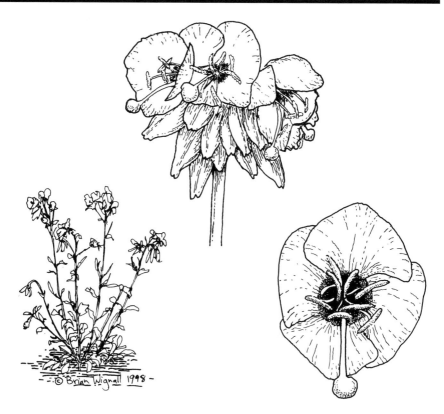

Camissonia claviformis
(Torr. & Frem.) Raven

Evening Primrose Family
Onagraceae

A spring-blooming annual of sandy flats and washes, this evening prim-rose has small, four-petaled flowers that turn pink or purplish as they wilt. Several varieties can be found in the Mojave Desert; the brown eyes of the common name can be seen in variety *claviformis*, which has white flowers with dark centers. Other varieties have yellow flowers or white flowers with-out dark centers. The stem tips often nod under their burden of flower buds.

Opening in late afternoon, the flowers attract small, solitary bees that come for pollen and nectar. One species of bee, *Andrena rozenii*, collects pollen from no other plant. These bees also mate among the blossoms of brown-eyed evening primrose, and make their nests in sandy places near the plants. Given its dependence on brown-eyed primrose, it seem appro-priate that *Andrena rozenii* is its major pollinator. Hawkmoths also visit the flowers, but their long tongues enable them to extract nectar without polli-nating flowers in return.

Dune evening primrose

Oenothera deltoides
Torr. & Frem.

Evening Primrose Family
Onagraceae

Dune evening primrose, a spring-blooming annual of dunes and sandy flats, is easily recognized by the large, white flowers with four heart-shaped petals. The hole in center of the flower is the opening of the floral tube. Poking out of the tube is a threadlike style with four yellow stigmas arranged in a cross. Around the style are eight nodding stamens. Opening around sunset and wilting by mid-morning of the following day, the fragrant blossoms of dune evening primrose attract a variety of hawkmoths. The long tongues of these stout-bodied moths are well suited for probing the floral tubes for nectar. As the moth hovers before an open flower, it brushes against the stamens and picks up long threads of pollen on its legs and underside. When the moth moves to the next flower, the pollen threads adhere to the very sticky stigma.

White bear poppy

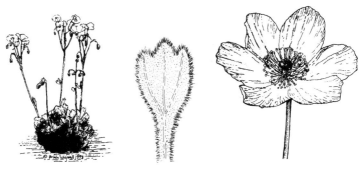

Arctomecon merriami
Cov.

Poppy Family
Papaveraceae

The name "bear poppy" refers to the long, white hairs that make the leaves as shaggy as a bear's pelage. The large flower has four (sometimes six) white petals; like those of many poppies, they wilt as soon as the flower is cut from the plant. The leaves are clustered in a rosette at the base of the single flowering stalk, which bears only one or sometimes several flowers. Bear poppy is perennial and flowers in spring. *Arctomecon merriami* was named by Frederic Coville, a botanist who discovered the species on an early scientific expedition to Death Valley.

The Las Vegas bear poppy, *Arctomecon californica* Torr. & Frem., grows in the Nevada portion of the Mojave Desert. It too has a basal rosette of shaggy leaves atop a perennial taproot; its yellow flowers are borne on slender, leafless stalks in spring. John C. Fremont, explorer, self-promoter, and eventually territorial governor of Arizona, discovered this species in the Las Vegas valley while crossing and recrossing the western United States in search of feasible routes from the Missouri frontier to the Pacific Coast.

Although you might see many plants at one location or another, bear poppies are rare and getting rarer. To keep from becoming extinct, bear poppies need ample seed production. Many seeds are lost to ants and other hazards; annual seed production is large enough, however, that normal predation does not hurt the species. Abnormal predation, as when people pick the flowers and seed pods, does hurt, because the plants do not take into account this kind of loss. Every flower that a person picks represents hundreds of seeds that will not fall to the ground. Because a bear poppy plant produces only a few flowers each year, the loss of even one flower matters a great deal. Fewer seeds mean fewer seedlings, and fewer seedlings mean that old plants are not replaced as they die. The damage done by thoughtless collectors thus feeds upon itself until the population is gone.

It is illegal to collect bear poppy flowers, seeds, and plants, nor is there much point in doing so. The seeds germinate poorly, the flowers wilt immediately, and transplants seldom survive.

Prickly poppy

Argemone munita
Durand & Hilg.

Poppy Family
Papaveraceae

Prickly poppies can be common in disturbed places such as roadsides, abandoned fields, and overgrazed pastures. Except for the large, white, crinkled petals, all parts of the plant, even the flower buds, are prickly. At one time, botanists divided this species into several different subspecies according to the number of prickles per square centimeter of stem: 0 to 10, 10 to 30, 50 to 80, and so forth. Eventually, a new generation of taxonomists decided that prickliness varied continuously rather than discretely; in other words, many specimens possessed an intermediate number of prickles and could not be fit into the predetermined categories. As a result, botanists no longer segregate *Argemone munita* into subspecies.

When broken, the fresh stems exude yellow sap. Because the sap is poisonous, cattle do not eat the plants, and this is why prickly poppies multiply rapidly on overgrazed ranges. Prickly poppy has a number of Spanish and Indian common names, including *chicalote, cardo santo campestre,* and *hierba loca.* An abundance of common names often suggests that a plant is widely used or greatly valued. Prickly poppy has been used in folk medicine to make eye drops, purgatives, and antiseptics. The plants are highly toxic, however, and many deaths have been attributed to their misuse.

Desert anemone

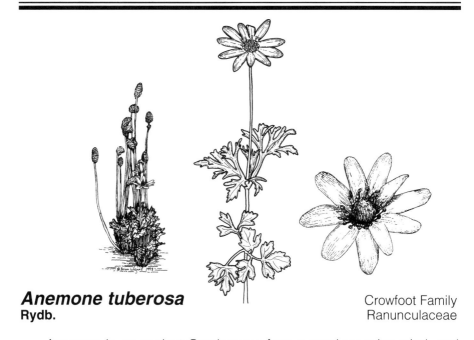

Anemone tuberosa
Rydb.

Crowfoot Family
Ranunculaceae

Anemone is an ancient Greek name from a word meaning wind, and anemones are sometimes called windflowers. Most anemones in the western United States are plants of shady, moist habitats or high elevations or both. *Anemone tuberosa* is the only one that grows in arid places. The succulent flowers, stems, and deeply cut leaves are not particularly resistant to the drying effects of heat and wind. It therefore behooves desert anemones to get an early start on the spring, before the days are really hot. Unlike spring-blooming annuals that depend on leafy rosettes to supply the carbohydrates needed for rapid growth of the flowering stalk, desert anemone relies on its tuberous root. Whereas leaves cannot supply much carbohydrate until the days are mild, tubers can furnish food for growth even when the soil is relatively cool. Desert anemones tend to grow in the shade of boulders or in other moist microhabitats. This too helps conserve water until the flowers have finished blooming.

Desert anemone cannot be found every spring; apparently the plants require ample rain in order to flower. In those years when it does appear, desert anemone is among the earliest bloomers. Instead of petals, the flowers have white or pale pink sepals. At the center of the flower are numerous stamens and pistils. When fertilized, the pistils develop into furry, one-seeded fruits that cling together in a conical bundle at the top of the stem. By the time the fruits have dispersed, the stem and leaves have dried out. The tuber remains underground, waiting for another series of good cool-season rains.

© Brian Wignall 1998

Claytonia perfoliata
Willd.

Portulaca Family
Portulacaceae

This is one wildflower that virtually identifies itself. No other desert annual has tiny white flowers dangling from the center of a saucer-shaped disk. Morphologically, the disk represents a pair of stem leaves, fused along their margins. Floppy, long-stalked leaves form a rosette at the base of the flowering stalk. Miner's lettuce grows in seasonally moist, shaded canyon bottoms, often in the protection of boulders or shrubs.

Taxonomists have described several different subspecies of *Claytonia perfoliata*. Ideally, subspecies should not only appear distinct from one another, they should also occupy separate geographical ranges. But in the case of miner's lettuce, the plants wholly fail to cooperate with taxonomists' needs. For one thing, the appearance of an individual plant reflects its circumstances to an unusual degree; the size and shape of leaves, the length of the flowering stalks, and even the number of flowers can change according to the amount of moisture and sunlight received. For another, the so-called subspecies tend to hybridize, bringing together in one population traits that would otherwise remain distinct. The situation is further confused by the existence of populations that are entirely self-pollinating and that overlap in distribution with cross-pollinating populations.

Sacred datura

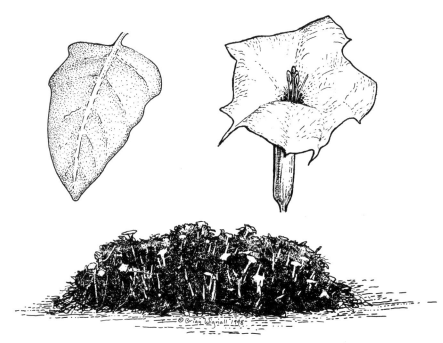

Datura wrightii
Regel

Figwort Family
Scrophulariaceae

The extravagant white flowers of sacred datura, often tinged with lavender on the margins, are sweetly scented. They are open at dusk and close the next morning. Hawkmoths with long tongues are the major pollinators. All parts of the plant, including the nectar, contain alkaloids, a class of chemicals that give sacred datura its well-known hallucinogenic and toxic properties. Moths that visit the flowers become visibly intoxicated, and although the moths apparently suffer no permanent damage, children have died from sucking the nectar. A number of teenagers have poisoned themselves, sometimes fatally, by using sacred datura to induce hallucinations, not realizing that the hallucinogenic dose is very close to the lethal dose. Native Americans used various species of datura for easing pain and for healing sores and boils; well-aware of its lethal potential, they generally applied the leaves or buds externally as poultices.

Sacred datura is sometimes called thorn apple, a reference to the seed pods, which are about the size and shape of golf balls but much more prickly. Jimson weed is yet another common name. The plants can be annual or perennial and are found along roads and in other disturbed places.

Weakstem mariposa

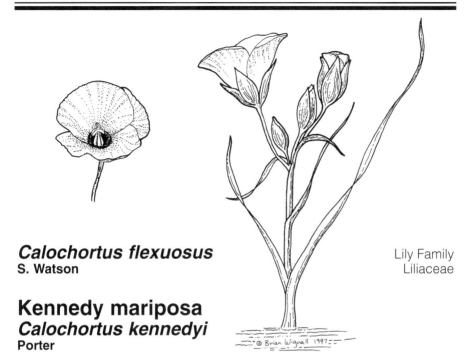

Calochortus flexuosus
S. Watson

Lily Family
Liliaceae

Kennedy mariposa
Calochortus kennedyi
Porter

© Brian Wignall 1997

Of the 65 species of mariposa lily in western North America and Central America, California has 43. Most are to be found in grassy or wooded habitats, but a few are able to survive in the desert. Mariposa lilies grow from bulbs, like many of their Lily Family relatives. Bulbs are basically food-storage organs. Any sugars manufactured by the leaves and not used in flowering are shunted to the bulb, where they are stored as starch. When conditions are right, the bulb sends up a flowering stalk and several leaves, using stored energy to fuel the process.

Weakstem mariposa has, as its name implies, a wavy stem that sprawls on the ground or clambers into shrubs. One to six bell-shaped flowers are borne on slender stalks that are also wavy. Each flower has three fan-shaped, white or purple petals that are banded with yellow. Kennedy mariposa (also called Kennedy lily) has erect stems and brilliantly colored petals; in variety _munzii_ they are yellow, in variety _kennedyi_, vermilion. In both weakstem mariposa and Kennedy mariposa, the dark spot at the base of each petal is a specialized gland known as a nectary. It secretes minute amounts of nectar for insect visitors, many of which pollinate the flowers in return. So distinctive are the nectary glands that an expert can identify certain species of mariposa lily by a single petal.

These lilies flower in spring. They are protected by law and should not be picked or dug from the ground.

67

Desert lily

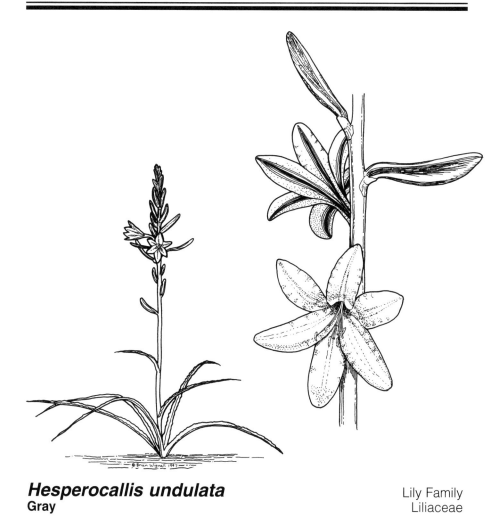

Hesperocallis undulata
Gray

Lily Family
Liliaceae

The long, undulating leaves of desert lily appear on pebbly or sandy flats in late winter or early spring. Within a month or so, the large bulbs, buried deep in the ground, send up sturdy flowering stalks bearing large, white, trumpet-shaped blossoms that look like Easter lilies. Hawkmoths, attracted by the intensely sweet fragrance of the flowers, are probably the most important pollinators.

In parts of its range, desert lily is known as ajo lily. Ajo is Spanish for garlic, and the name probably refers to one potential use of the edible bulbs. Like all wild lilies, this one is protected by law and should not be dug or picked.

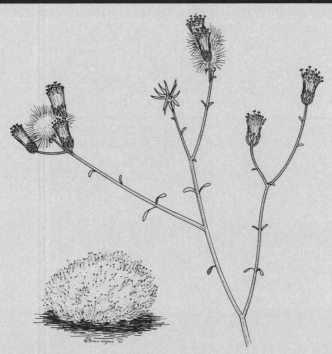

Bebbia juncea
(Benth.) Greene

Sunflower Family
Asteraceae

Sweetbush, a rounded shrub to four feet in height, looks a bit like Mormon tea because of the tightly packed, twiggy stems. Old stems are white-barked; young stems are ashy green with faint striations. The slender leaves are sparse and short-lived; much of the year, sweetbush is entirely leafless, relying on the green stems for photosynthesis. Caterpillars of the Wright metalmark, a desert butterfly, sensibly rely for their food not on the ephemeral leaves but on the surface of the stem.

Small orange or yellow-orange flowers, densely clustered into thimble-sized heads, appear at almost any time of year, given enough rain. They are sweetly fragrant and attract many bees and butterflies, some of which pollinate the flowers in moving from plant to plant. The flowers also attract chuckwallas, wide-bodied lizards of vegetarian habits, which eat large quantities of the blossoms. The tuft of hairs, called a "pappus," atop each seed is a dispersal mechanism. As the seeds ripen, the bracts around the flower head curl backward, exposing the seeds. Wind catches the pappus and blows the seeds away.

Sweetbush grows best where the soil is somewhat disturbed, as in washes, along roads, and on roadcuts.

Rubber rabbitbrush

© Brian Wignall 93'

Chrysothamnus nauseosus
(Pall.) Britt.

Sunflower Family
Asteraceae

Rubber rabbitbrush blooms abundantly in the fall, splashing roadsides and washes with golden yellow. Multitudes of bees, wasps, and butterflies visit the flowers, which bloom at a time of year when few other nectar and pollen sources are available. The wandlike, yellow-green stems have a somewhat fetid odor when crushed.

There are twenty-two different subspecies of rubber rabbitbrush. Some are quite distinctive; others are hard to tell apart. Where several subspecies occur in the same general region, they tend to occupy different habitats. One might prefer mountain slopes, the other valley bottoms, or one might tolerate salty soils, the other not. This kind of physical separation limits hybridization and keeps the subspecies distinct. A subspecies is an incipient species; given enough time and isolation, it may evolve into a distinct entity.

Rubber rabbitbrush has a variety of traditional and nontraditional uses. Native Americans made a yellow dye from the flowering branches and a medicinal tea from the leaves. The stem sap, which is almost three percent rubber, has been investigated as an emergency substitute for imported natural rubber.

Chrysothamnus paniculatus
(Gray) H. M. Hall

Sunflower Family
Asteraceae

Chrysothamnus means "golden shrub" in Greek and applies to all species in the genus. Applying only to this particular species, the word *paniculatus* refers to the arrangement of the flower heads. A "panicle" has several orders of branching: the main stem branches into stalks that bear stalklets to which the flowers are attached.

Locally abundant in gravelly washes, Mojave rabbitbrush makes billowing waves of yellow when the plants bloom in autumn. The threadlike leaves are shiny from resins. The stems are frequently banded with black, either from insect attack or fungal disease. Like rubber rabbitbrush, this species contains natural rubber of fair quality.

Bladder pod

© Brian Wignall

Isomeris arborea
Nutt.

Caper Family
Capparidaceae

This three- to five-foot shrub, named after the inflated fruits, is one of several desert plants referred to as bladder pod. Prospectors knew it as burro fat. Borne on long, slender stalks like pendant teardrops, the fruits are surprisingly light for their size. When ripe, they turn into papery balloons that tumble across the ground, thus dispersing the seeds. The spring-blooming flowers are mustard yellow with long stamens and pistils. When rubbed or crushed, the leaves and stems smell something like dirty socks.

A small white butterfly, Becker's white, lays its eggs on bladder pod. You might find its green-and-orange caterpillars on the leaves in the spring. These caterpillars also eat various kinds of wild mustards. Bladder pod and wild mustard belong to different but closely related plant families, and their chemical composition is evidently similar enough that Becker's whites can thrive on both.

Bladder pod blooms intermittently throughout the year. The plants grow best in disturbed situations such as roadsides and sandy washes.

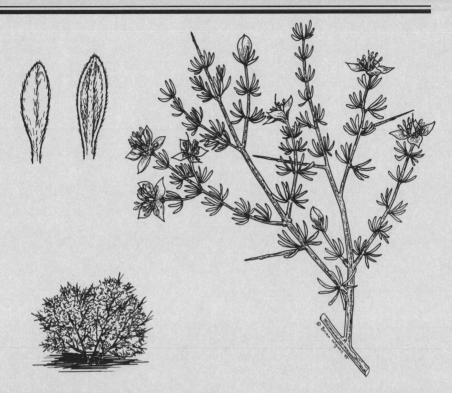

Coleogyne ramosissima
Torr.

Rose Family
Rosaceae

Its sooty gray bark makes this intricately branched shrub appear black from a distance, thus the common name. When it grows in pure stands, as it often does, blackbrush makes for a rather somber landscape. When they bloom in April and May, however, the shrubs are quite pretty. There are no petals; the four sepals, all bright yellow on the inside, take over the function of petals, attracting pollinators to the cluster of stamens and pistil in the center of the flower. The tiny leaves are gray and arise in pairs on the thorn-tipped branches.

Blackbrush grows on rocky hills and canyon slopes. It tends to grow where rainfall is rather high for a desert—from ten to twenty inches a year. The seeds germinate only when spring rains are unusually early. Even when this happens—and it is an uncommon event—most seedlings fail to survive their first year. The result is a community in which individuals only rarely become established. Because the shrubs grow slowly and live to a great age (well over one hundred years), the seedlings that do survive maintain their position for a long time.

Brittlebush

Encelia farinosa
A. Gray

Sunflower Family
Asteraceae

At its best, brittlebush is a hemisphere of blue-green leaves; at its worst, it is a collection of white stems to which a few withered, gray leaves cling like bedraggled flags. The plants alternate between these two personalities on a seasonal basis. Winter rains bring out the best—bushy canopies of blue-green leaves that photosynthesize at a rapid rate. As the soil dries out, most leaves fall. The few that remain are small and gray-green. They photosynthesize, too, but at a much lower rate because the gray hairs reflect much of the incoming sunlight. Deflecting solar radiation keeps the leaves from becoming too hot. These white or gray leaves cling to the stems for many months unless the soil becomes extremely dry, whereupon they drop. Because drought induces dormancy in the stem tip, no new leaves can be produced until rains have moistened the soil once again. Then the cycle begins anew.

When brittlebush blooms in spring, entire hillsides turn yellow. The blossoms are large for a desert plant, about the size of a half-dollar. Each contains numerous disk flowers in the central medallion and about a dozen ray flowers on the perimeter. Butterflies, moths and small beetles pollinate the flowers. When broken, the stems exude a golden, resinous fluid. The Spanish common name for brittlebush, *incienso*, reminds us that this resin was once dried and burned as incense.

© Brian Wignall 93'

Encelia frutescens
(A. Gray) A. Gray

Sunflower Family
Asteraceae

A rounded shrub about two or three feet in height, rayless encelia is notable for its brittle, white stems and rough, dark green leaves. The plants colonize roadsides and washes.

Rayless encelia puts out its bright yellow, bell-shaped flower heads whenever rainfall provides the opportunity. Unlike brittlebush, its grayer relative, the leaves of green brittlebush lack a dense coat of hairs. They cannot adjust their photosynthetic pace to suit the climate. When soil moisture is high, the plants produce abundant new leaves, which photosynthesize at a rapid rate. As the soil dries out, the leaves drop, and the plants become dormant until the next rainfall.

Cooper goldenbush

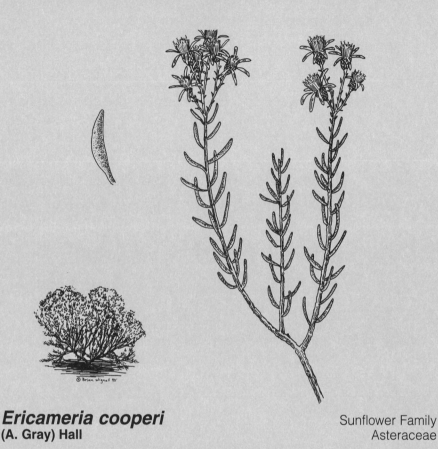

Ericameria cooperi
(A. Gray) Hall

Sunflower Family
Asteraceae

Between April and June, this low, rounded shrub becomes a mass of yellow flowers. Blooming is probably triggered by winter rains, which occur more or less reliably across the range of this species. In southern Arizona, turpentine bush (*Ericameria laricifolia* (A. Gray) Shinners), a close relative and near-twin of Cooper goldenbush, blooms in the autumn, responding to the abundant summer rains characteristic of its region.

The evergreen leaves of Cooper goldenbush are clustered toward the branch tips. They are short, flat, and narrow, a configuration that minimizes water loss. Small resin glands, visible to the naked eye as dark pinpoints on the leaves, release a pungent odor when crushed.

Cooper goldenbush grows on rocky slopes and gravelly plains, frequently with Joshua trees. It does not tolerate disturbance well, and after the landscape has been plowed or bladed, Cooper goldenbush might not reappear on the site for several decades or longer.

Baileya pleniradiata
A. Gray

Sunflower Family
Asteraceae

Three species of desert marigold can be found in the Mojave Desert: *Baileya pleniradiata*, *Baileya multiradiata*, and *Baileya pauciradiata*. Although all possess yellow flower heads, felty or woolly foliage, and a strong preference for roadsides and sandy washes, a keen eye can tell them apart fairly readily. *Baileya pauciradiata* is a poor thing compared to its siblings, having only four to eight ray flowers compared to their fifteen or more (generally many more). This is more or less what the species name (which means "few-rayed" in Latin) states. The other two species differ less strikingly; the flower stalks of *Baileya multiradiata* are four to eight inches long, and the leaves are mostly clustered at the base of the plant, whereas flowers stalks of *Baileya pleniradiata* are four inches or less, and leaves are both clustered at the base and scattered along the stem. The Latin names of these two desert marigolds are also descriptive, meaning "many-rayed" and "plentifully rayed."

Desert sunflower

© Brian Wignall 1997

Geraea canescens
Torr. & Gray

Sunflower Family
Asteraceae

Desert sunflower is one of the first annuals to bloom in the spring, appearing on gravelly flats and sandy plains as early as January. The plants are generally robust, reaching two feet or more in height. The leaves and stems bristle with short, stiff hairs. Like all members of the Sunflower Family, desert sunflower packs small individual flowers into many-flowered heads. Desert sunflower heads are almost two inches diameter. The disk flowers in the center of the head and the ray flowers around the perimeter are all bright yellow.

Many kinds of insects might visit the flowers, but there is one, a native bee, that depends solely on desert sunflower for pollen. The bee times its emergence from underground burrows to coincide with the blooming of desert sunflower. Heavy rain—at least an inch—is necessary for desert sunflower seeds to germinate in fall or winter. The seedlings grow rapidly during winter warm spells, more slowly when days and nights are cold. The same climatic signals that trigger germination and flowering of desert sunflower probably also cue the bees that rely on them.

Gutierrezia sarothrae
(Pursh) Britt.

Sunflower Family
Asteraceae

In full flower, snakeweed is a yellow dome about two feet high. Each individual flower is miniscule, but because a dozen flowers are combined into a single head and a single plant might have a thousand heads, the result is a showy display. In the autumn, fields and pastures turn yellow when snakeweed blooms.

Snakeweed can become abundant where too many cattle feed in a limited area. Since cattle eat grasses in preference to snakeweed, the latter multiplies as the former decrease. Even sheep and goats, notorious for eating just about anything, avoid snakeweed if possible.

Medicinal uses of the foliage have included teas for treating stomach disorders, rheumatism, and malaria and poultices for snakebite. Two additional common names—resin weed and turpentine weed—refer to the odor of the narrow, green leaves. Yet another common name, matchweed, comes from the ease with which the resinous stems catch fire.

Desert dandelion

Malacothrix glabrata
A. Gray

Sunflower Family
Asteraceae

Like many spring wildflowers in the Mojave Desert, desert dandelion is a winter annual. To germinate, the seeds require cool (but not cold) soils and at least an inch of rain, a combination of circumstances that is most likely to happen in autumn or early winter. The seedlings rapidly produce a number of leaves, then spend the winter as ground-hugging rosettes. If the winter is unusually cold or the spring unusually dry, the rosettes do not survive. Under better circumstances, the warming temperatures of spring encourage the rosettes to bolt, that is, to produce buds, flowers, and fruits in rapid succession.

Desert dandelion belongs to the Sunflower Family and, within that family, to the subfamily Liguliflorae. All members of this subfamily have milky sap and heads composed entirely of ray flowers. Each ray is a single flower and comes equipped with pistils and stamens. The five teeth at the tip of the ray represent vestigial flower lobes. During millions of years of evolution, the Sunflower Family became ever more specialized as individual flowers were reduced to florets, then crowded together in heads; the substitution of tiny teeth for flower lobes might have come about as a way of packing florets into a head as efficiently as possible.

Blooming in spring, desert dandelion can be abundant on sandy soils. The flowers are pale yellow or white. The common name comes from the toothed, dandelion-like leaves. Unlike tackstem, desert dandelion is virtually without hairs.

Pygmy cedar

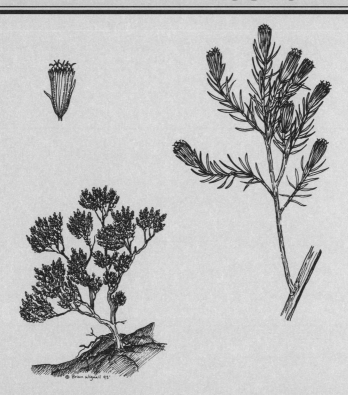

Peucephyllum schottii

Sunflower Family
Asteraceae

Pygmy cedar, sometimes called desert fir, is neither a cedar nor a fir but a three- to four-foot-high shrub in the large and diverse Sunflower Family. The dark green, needle-shaped leaves are clustered toward the stem tips, giving the plants their coniferlike appearance. The scientific name also acknowledges this resemblance—*Peucephyllym* is Greek for "fir leaf."

The bell-shaped flower heads contain about twenty yellow disk flowers apiece. At low elevations where winters are mild, flowering can begin as early as December. In locations where winters are colder, blooming can be delayed until March. The bristly achenes (dry, one-seeded fruits) disperse in late spring and summer.

Because the uppermost branches suffer frost damage when temperatures drop only slightly below freezing, pygmy cedar is most frequent where winters are mild. Even there, the shrubs often cling to cliffs, which offer some protection from frost by absorbing heat during the day and radiating it at night. Where the climate is very dry, pygmy cedar grows in sandy washes where runoff after storms provides extra moisture.

81

Turtleback

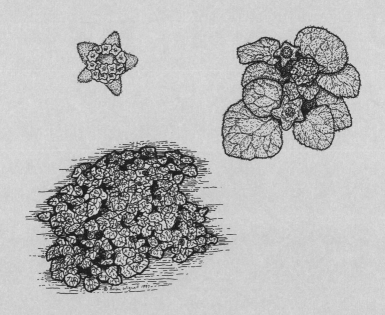

Psathyrotes ramosissima
(Torr.) A. Gray

Sunflower Family
Asteraceae

If turtles had gray-green, yellow-polka-dotted shells and never moved from their appointed places, they would look a lot like turtleback, an annual that forms hemispherical cushions on road shoulders, sandy washes, and desert flats. Other common names—desert velvet and velvet rosette—refer to the velvety hairs of the spoon-shaped leaves. When crushed, the foliage smells like turpentine. About two dozen yellow-orange disk flowers are packed into each small flower head.

Lacking adaptations to the desert environment, most annual wildflowers cannot tolerate heat and drought. For this reason, they germinate and grow during the cooler, moister months. Such plants are often said to be drought-evaders rather than drought-tolerators. Turtleback, however, appears to be one desert annual that is prepared for the worst. The velvety coat of hairs reflects sunlight, which keeps the leaves from scorching. The cushionlike habit could also be an adaptation to its arid environment; the dense shade thus created probably retards water loss from the soil.

Turtleback can be distinguished from the closely related *Psathyrotes annua* (Nutt.) A. Gray by examining the bracts of the flower heads. The outermost bracts of turtleback heads are much wider than the inner ones, whereas *Psathyrotes annua* bracts are all about the same size.

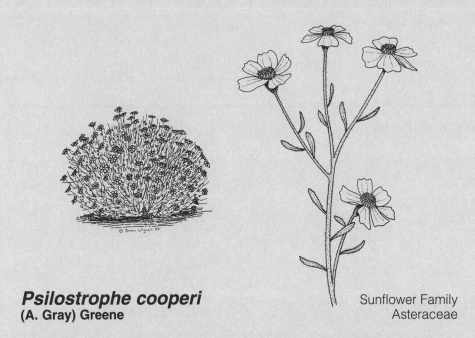

Psilostrophe cooperi
(A. Gray) Greene

Sunflower Family
Asteraceae

Paper flower, also known as paper daisy, blooms in response to good winter or summer rains. The one-foot-high plants are perennial but sometimes bloom the first year. They can be found on road shoulders, dirt roads, abandoned fields, old townsites, and other disturbed places. The stems and narrow leaves are white or gray-green with felty hairs. Flower heads about the size of a quarter are borne in groups of one to three at the stem tips. Both the disk flowers in the center of each head and the ray flowers at the perimeter are bright yellow. All the flowers are attached to tiny green ovaries that ripen into dry, one-seeded fruits called achenes.

The common name of this wildflower comes from the ray flowers, which become dried and sun-bleached as they age. Instead of falling as the achenes ripen, the rays persist, and eventually become papery wings that catch in the wind, dispersing the seed to a more distant site. The disk flowers wither normally, leaving behind a clutch of achenes that spill to the ground when ripe. Paper flower thus has a dual dispersal mode—some seeds fall in a spot that has already proved suitable, and some attempt to colonize suitable places elsewhere. Much risk is involved either way. Ray achenes run the risk of not landing in the kind of disturbed sites where paper flower thrives. Disk achenes might discover that other plants have fully occupied the available space, leaving no room for new arrivals. By hedging its bets, paper flower increases the chances that at least a few seeds will germinate on suitable sites.

Fiddleneck

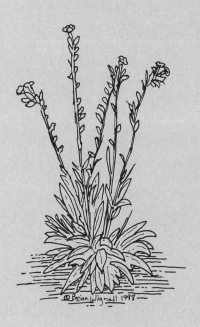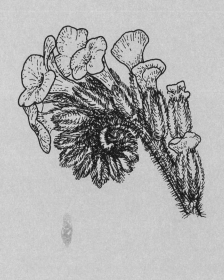

Amsinckia tessellata
A. Gray

Borage Family
Boraginaceae

The flowering stalks of fiddleneck are coiled near the tip like the scroll of a violin. Stems and leaves bristle with spinelike hairs, a trait recorded in such common names as devil's lettuce and fireweed. The peculiar fruit comprises four pyramidal nutlets attached to a central axis. The cobblestone pattern on the nutlets reflects yet another common name, checker fiddleneck.

The small, orange and yellow flowers are probably self-pollinated. Because they require no exchange of pollen with neighboring plants, they are independent of insect pollinators and can produce a good seed crop even when pollinators are scarce. Moreover, when a seed is transported far away, it can germinate, flower, and set a new crop of seeds immediately, and each of those seeds can do the same the following year. In this way, a large population can be established quite rapidly.

Fiddleneck can be abundant, especially in disturbed sites such as old fields, roadsides, and pastures. The seeds and foliage contain alkaloids and high concentrations of nitrate, making them poisonous to livestock and probably also to humans.

Prince's plume

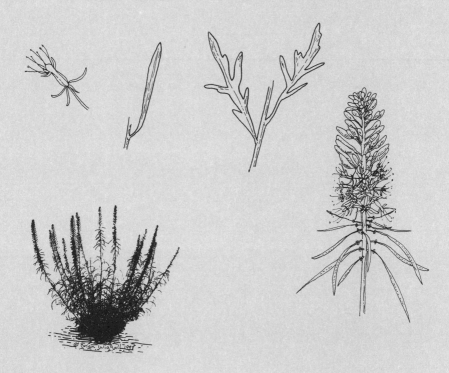

Stanleya pinnata
(Pursh) Britt.

Mustard Family
Brassicaceae

The pale yellow flowers of prince's plume are so dense that a flowering stalk looks something like a yellow cattail. When in bloom, the stems can reach three to five feet in height. The flowers have four petals arranged in the shape of a cross. An older name for the Mustard Family—Cruciferae—means "cross-bearing." The long, narrow pods curve downward as they mature.

Prince's plume grows in a variety of habitats. At some sites, the plants take up the mineral selenium from the soil. Because selenium is similar in its chemical properties to sulfur, the plant simply substitutes selenium for sulfur in the production of amino acids, the building blocks of protein crucial to all living organisms. Although prince's plume can utilize selenium in place of sulfur, mammals cannot, and large amounts of selenium are toxic to livestock and humans.

Cottontop

Echinocactus polycephalus
Engelm. & Bigel.

Cactus Family
Cactaceae

The apex of this roly-poly cactus is woolly with white hairs, thus the common name. Showy, yellow flowers emerge from the woolly mat in July, and woolly-coated fruits appear about a month later. The fruits often persist on the plants for several more months.

Another common name, clustered barrel cactus, is equally descriptive because the stems are often clumped. Individual stems reach one to two feet in height and somewhat less in diameter. A small clump of four to six stems might be three feet in diameter. Just as a tree accumulates branches as it grows, so cottontop accumulates stems, and the number of stems in a clump is thus a rough indicator of age. One individual in the Grand Canyon was first photographed in 1890 when it had only a few stems. One hundred years later, still in good health, it was a behemoth with about thirty stems piled together like so many bowling balls.

Cottontop can be locally common on rocky flats and slopes. In the colder parts of their range, the plants often grow on south-facing cliff ledges; here they probably receive some protection from frost as sun-warmed bedrock releases heat at night. The woolly mat of hairs on the plant apex protects the tender growing point from low temperatures.

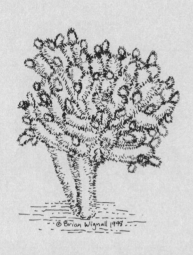

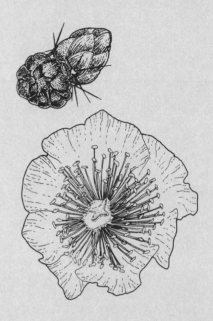

Opuntia echinocarpa
Engelm. & Bigel.

Cactus Family
Cactaceae

Like all chollas, this one is constructed of cylindrical stem segments called joints. In silver cholla, the joints are about one to one and one-half inches in diameter. From a distance, especially when backlit by the sun, the dense spine clusters make the plants look silvery or golden. Silver cholla can take the form of a small tree about two to five feet in height. Most cacti have showy flowers, but those of silver cholla are small and greenish-yellow. Chollas that have succulent, berrylike fruits depend on fruit-eating animals to disperse the seeds. Silver chollas is not of this type. Its species name, *echinocarpa*, is Greek for "hedgehog fruited," and the fruits are indeed dry and spiny, resembling burs rather than berries. Doubtless they behave like burs at times, hitching rides on the legs and feet of passing animals.

Silver cholla grows on plains and in sandy washes. After the plants die, the fleshy tissue rots rather quickly with the help of fruit flies and fungi. What remains then is a skeleton made of woody cylinders that represent the trunk and branches. The cylinders are punctured like sieves with a regular pattern of holes. Termites eventually devour cholla wood, enriching the soil with organic matter and nutrients.

Grizzly bear prickly pear

© Brian Wignall 1998

Opuntia erinacea
Engelm. & Bigel.
var. erinacea

Cactus Family
Cactaceae

This low, spreading cactus, known as grizzly bear prickly pear, old man prickly pear, or Mojave prickly pear, is swathed in flexible, downward pointing spines up to eight inches long. The yellow flowers appear in late spring. In some populations, the flowers are pink or reddish-purple as well as yellow. Flower color is notoriously variable in the genus *Opuntia*, and the different species can seldom be identified from flower color alone.

The pads grow in clusters from a large underground root. If left undisturbed, these clusters can reach a diameter of three or four feet. As individual pads age, they deteriorate and die, but the root continues to produce new pads nearby. Over time, the plant slowly shifts its position as new pads succeed old. A cluster of pads can occupy the same spot for a century or more.

Coyote melon

Cucurbita palmata
S. Watson

Gourd Family
Cucurbitaceae

Vines are not particularly common in deserts, perhaps because there is not much to climb. Coyote melon clambers up mesquite trees and fence posts when possible and sprawls across the ground when not. More or less heart-shaped in outline, the leaf blade is deeply cut into five triangular lobes. Leaves and stems alike are rough from stiff hairs. The large yellow flowers are bell-shaped and look like typical squash blossoms. The spherical fruits are about the size of a tennis ball. When immature, they are green, faintly striped with white. As they ripen, the rinds turn yellow, then tan, and the seeds rattle inside.

Like the flowers of most squashes, those of coyote melon open early in the morning, sometimes before dawn. The squash and gourd bees, which rely exclusively on the pollen and nectar of wild gourds, are up in time to pollinate the flowers. Sometimes the bees spend the rest of the day asleep inside the blossoms.

Compounds called cucurbitacins make the gourds extremely bitter. Even a tiny taste can linger unpleasantly in the mouth for hours. In large quantities, cucurbitacins can be toxic. Pueblo Indians reportedly used the juice as an insect repellent.

Spiny senna

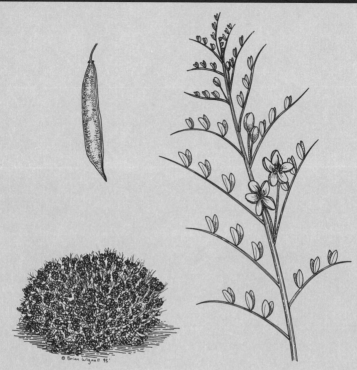

Senna armata
(S. Wats.) Irwin & Barnb.

Pea Family
Fabaceae

In the tropical parts of Mexico and Central America, sennas are graceful trees with luxuriantly leafy canopies and brilliant yellow flower clusters. In adapting to the desert, spiny senna, a two-foot-tall shrub, has kept the yellow flowers and discarded the rest. Since water is scarce in deserts, many desert plants, spiny senna among them, produce only ephemeral leaves. Such plants rely on their green stems to do the work of photosynthesis, producing the sugars necessary for growth.

In the spring the bare stems put out flowering shoots adorned with pretty five-petaled flowers and sparse leaves. Each leaf is composed of four to six pairs of leaflets that drop within a month or two. Afterwards, the leaf axis remains as a feeble spine. Spininess is common among desert plants; no one is quite sure why. Defense against herbivores is one suggestion. Another is that spininess is somehow a consequence of the arid environment. What is certain is that desert plants arrive at spininess by different routes. Some, like catclaw, develop spines by modification of tiny leaf bracts called stipules. Others, like spiny senna, employ the leaf stalk or the leaf axis, usually after the leaves drop.

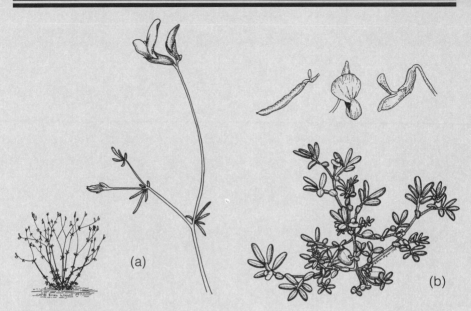

Lotus rigidus (a)
(Benth.) E. Greene

Pea Family
Fabaceae

Hairy lotus
Lotus strigosus (b)
(Nutt.) E. Greene

Rock pea is a spring-blooming shrub about two feet in height. The stems are woody at the base. Three- or four-parted leaves are scattered along the stems at fairly wide intervals. The inch-long flowers are yellow, tinged with red; one petal, the banner, is markedly larger than the other four. One to three flowers are clustered at the tip of long, leafless stalks. The fruits are typical legume pods; they turn brown as they ripen, then twist open, scattering the seeds.

Growing on rocky slopes and in washes, rock pea is sometimes eaten by desert tortoises, which have been observed to climb into the branches and stand on their hind feet in an effort to get at the flowers and pods.

Hairy lotus is a winter annual that can be abundant on sandy flats, at roadsides, and in washes. Its yellow flowers are about half as long as those of rock pea, and its stems are often pressed to the ground, radiating from the base. The leaf comprises four to nine leaflets attached in pairs to a flattened axis. Desert tortoises are fond of hairy lotus; annual wildflowers make up a large proportion of their diet in the spring.

Small-flowered blazing star

© Brian Wignall 1998

Mentzelia albicaulis
Hook.

Loasa Family
Loasaceae

A white-stemmed annual with small, buttercup-yellow flowers, blazing star can be common in sandy or gravelly places in spring. The stems, leaves, and seed pods feel like sandpaper to the touch and detach easily from the plant, sticking to socks, pant legs, and fur. Under magnification you can see the barbed hairs that turn plant fragments into hitchhikers. Using animals as unwitting agents of seed dispersal, small-flowered blazing star manages to send some of its seeds to distant places. Chances are that conditions for germination and survival will be no better there than here; on the other hand, desert rain varies so much from place to place that long-distance dispersal sometimes places seeds in spots where, despite the unfavorable odds, good rains finally happen.

California poppy

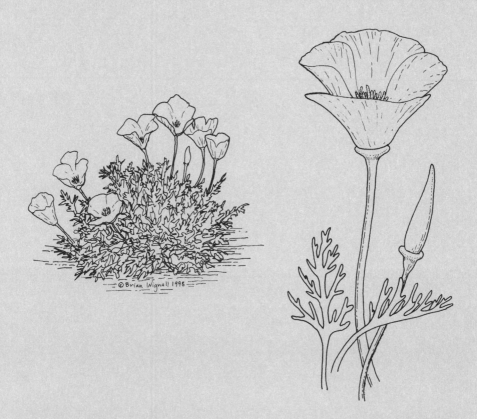

© Brian Wignall 1995

Eschscholzia californica
Cham.

Poppy Family
Papaveraceae

After heavy winter rains, California poppy can be abundant on rocky slopes and gravelly flats. The brilliant yellow-orange flowers are borne singly on slender, leafless stalks that arise from a cluster of waxy-looking, fernlike leaves. The four silken petals fall at the end of the day. On cloudy days, the flowers might fail to open. As many as ninety different varieties and sub-species have been described and named, a consequence of great variability within the species. For example, the plants can be annual or perennial, upright or spreading, and anywhere from three to eighteen inches in height. Flowers can be pure orange, or yellow-orange with dark orange centers, or even cream-colored.

Desert gold poppy

Eschscholzia glyptosperma
E. Greene

Poppy Family
Papaveraceae

Desert gold poppy, a yellow-flowered annual that blooms in spring, is a diminutive version of the California poppy with shorter flower stalks (generally no more than five or eight inches in height), fewer basal leaves, and smaller flowers (no more than one inch in diameter). These water-thrifty traits enable desert gold poppy to thrive where conditions are too harsh for the lusher California poppy. One such place is desert pavement, those broad, arid flats entirely covered with pebbles. Under the pebbles, the soil is somewhat water-repellent, so rain penetrates very slowly if at all. In addition, the soil often contains more sodium than most plants can tolerate.

94

© Brian Wignall 1998

Linanthus aureus
(Nutt.) E. Greene

Phlox Family
Polemoniaceae

    The funnel-shaped flowers of golden linanthus are only an inch long, but they seem huge in comparison to the threadlike stems. In a good spring, the lemon-yellow of the blossoms colors arid flats and slopes as effectively as buttercups color a marsh or meadow. Golden linanthus has reduced all of its green matter to a bare minimum. Not only are the stems about as slender as stems can get, the leaves are few and widely spaced. Each leaf is palmately lobed, like a hand with its four fingers and thumb; in keeping with the over-all reduction of surface area, the palm has been virtually eliminated. Two subspecies of this annual wildflower can be found in the Mojave Desert: flowers of subspecies *aureus* are yellow throughout, those of subspecies *decorus* have whitish lobes and a maroon throat.

Desert trumpet

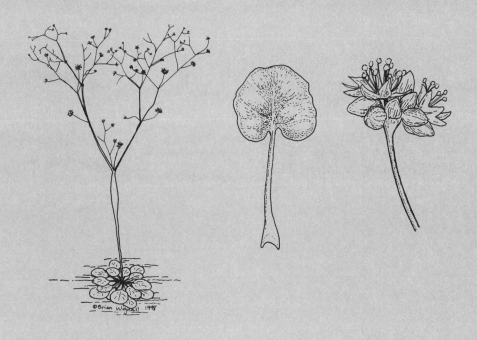

©Brian Wignall 1998

Eriogonum inflatum
Torr. & Frem.

Buckwheat Family
Polygonaceae

Common on gravelly slopes, along roads, and on sandy flats, desert trumpet is one of many wild buckwheats in California. Its most distinctive feature is the upright stem that tapers from a swollen apex to a narrow base. Above the apex, the stem divides into many fine branchlets that bear conical bracts, each containing a few tiny, yellow flowers. There are at least two schools of thought regarding the cause and function of the swollen apex. One school asserts that a particular kind of wasp deposits her eggs inside young, green stems, which then enlarge and harden to become a gall in which the wasp larvae can develop. Another school believes that the enlarged apex serves a physiological function having to do with storage of carbon dioxide and that wasps or other insects colonize the inflated stem after it is formed. Taxonomists, ignoring this small controversy entirely, recognize two varieties of desert trumpet, one with swollen stems (variety *inflatum*), the other without (variety *deflatum*).

Twining snapdragon

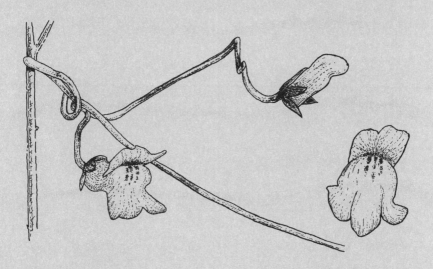

Antirrhinum filipes
Gray

Figwort Family
Scrophulariaceae

Desert snapdragons are much less flamboyant than the cultivated kind, but both belong to the genus *Antirrhinum*. Garden snapdragons, which are European imports, have been bred for large flower size, variety of color, and striking color combinations. Desert snapdragons live in the real world, so their flowers are exactly as large and colorful as necessary for survival and reproduction. If the flowers were too large, the plants would require extra water, and they could not survive in arid habitats. Their color patterns, although not flashy, perfectly serve the purpose of attracting native bees and guiding them to nectar. Most desert snapdragons are leafy-stemmed annuals with small, trumpet-shaped flowers in shades of purple and white. Twining snapdragon, an annual vine, has yellow and gold flowers spaced at long intervals on the twining stem.

Different vines climb in different ways. Some modify various plant parts (a branchlet or a leaf axis, for example) into claws or tendrils. Others climb by winding their stems around any convenient object. Some use the leaf stalks as a climbing device, and a few, such as twining snapdragon, actually use the flower stalks, or pedicels, curling them around the stems of woody plants. This is possible because the pedicels are thin and up to three or four inches long, much longer and thinner than those of any other native snapdragon.

Twining snapdragon is an infrequent annual of sandy flats and washes.

Yellow monkeyflower

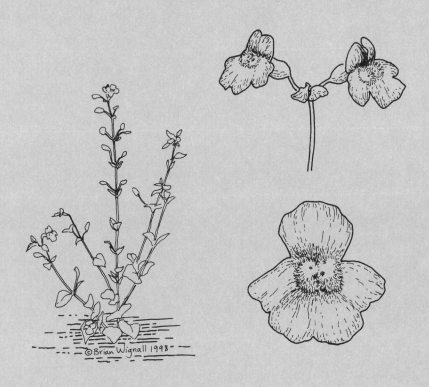

Mimulus guttatus
DC.

Figwort Family
Scrophulariaceae

Yellow monkeyflower, also called spotted monkeyflower, grows in streams, springs, and seeps. The stems root at the nodes, forming clumps on cliffs and among streambed rocks. Flowers are bright yellow and spotted with red in one variety, unspotted in another. The stigma is forked, and the two inner surfaces are sticky so that pollen can adhere to them. The two outer surfaces are dry and cannot capture pollen. When a bee enters the flower in search of nectar, it brushes against the stigma, and pollen on the bee's body adheres to the sticky lobes. The lobes then press themselves together so that only the dry sides are exposed. The bee contacts the anthers, takes nectar, and withdraws. No pollen from within the flower touches the closed stigmas as the bee leaves the blossom. In this way, the flowers promote cross-pollination and hinder self-pollination. Yellow monkeyflower blooms from spring to fall.

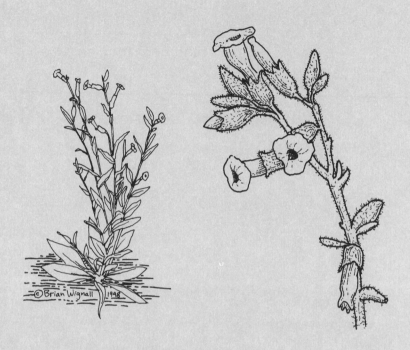

Nicotiana obtusifolia
Mart. & Gal.

Nightshade Family
Solanaceae

The genus Nicotiana is named after Jean Nicot, who introduced tobacco (*Nicotiana tabacum* L.) to France in the sixteenth century. Desert tobacco, like many other species in the genus, contains the alkaloid nicotine and was smoked by Native Americans, generally on ceremonial occasions and also to relieve lung congestion. As well as nicotine, wild tobaccos also contain anabasine, another highly toxic alkaloid. Native Americans used the leaves externally to treat headache and congestion.

The greenish-yellow or cream-colored flowers of desert tobacco are funnel-shaped and about an inch long. The plants are sometimes annual, sometimes perennial, depending on environment and climate. Glandular hairs make the foliage sticky. In outline, the leaves can be heart- or spoon-shaped. Some have broad stalks; others are attached directly to the stem.

Tree tobacco (*Nicotiana glauca* Graham), a small and slender tree native to South America, can be found along roads, in washes, and in other disturbed places. Its yellow flowers, borne on drooping branchlets, are two to four inches long. Hummingbirds visit them for nectar.

Creosotebush

Larrea tridentata
(Moc. & Sess.) Cav.

Caltrop Family
Zygophyllaceae

Native Americans used creosotebush as a drugstore. It provided medications for stiff limbs, sores, snake bites, menstrual cramps, and many other ills. As is often the case, the chemicals that produce efficacious medications are toxic in large doses, which means that creosotebush foliage is unpalatable to most insects and mammals. Exceptions include a small desert grasshopper and a walking stick that have adapted so thoroughly to the resinous leaves that they can eat nothing else.

An abundant shrub of gravelly plains, sandy flats, and rocky slopes, creosotebush is the quintessential desert plant. The resins on the leaves retard water loss, as does the habit of dropping some leaves during dry periods. Creosotebush can continue to photosynthesize long after the dryness of the soil has forced other plants into dormancy. When rainfall renews soil moisture, creosotebush responds rapidly with new stems and leaves.

Creosotebush lives to a great age. As old stems in the center of the plant die, new stems sprout on the perimeter. The resulting ring of stems, essentially a clone of the original plant, can easily survive for hundreds or even thousands of years.

When creosotebush blooms in spring, a multitude of insects, including dozens of species of native bees, visit the yellow, five-petaled blossoms.

Camissonia brevipes
(A. Gray) Raven

Evening Primrose Family
Onagraceae

Sundrops, also called suncups or yellow cups, has inch-wide flowers loosely clustered toward the top of the stem. The four petals and four sepals are attached around the top of the funnel-shaped hypanthium, or floral tube. The leaves are largely clustered at the base of the stem. Most are deeply and unevenly cut into lobes, the terminal lobe being about five times as long as the others.

A spring-flowering annual, sundrops can be abundant on sandy flats, in washes, and on rocky slopes.

Spring evening primrose

Oenothera primiveris
Gray

Evening Primrose Family
Onagraceae

An early spring wildflower found on gravelly flats and in washes, this evening primrose sometimes blooms before the last frost of winter. The pale yellow flowers have four heart-shaped petals. They open at dusk and crumple the next day, turning reddish as they wilt.

The seeds germinate in autumn and early winter. Seedlings quickly develop into ground-hugging rosettes of dandelion-like leaves. A sturdy taproot anchors the rosette and remains in place after the flowers and leaves have dried up. The woody seed pods remain in place, too, attached to an abbreviated stem.

Wire lettuce

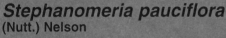

Stephanomeria pauciflora
(Nutt.) Nelson

Sunflower Family
Asteraceae

In English, wire lettuce is also known as desert straw and desert milk-aster; the Seri Indians of northwestern Sonora call it by names meaning "rootless plant" and "plant that thinks it is a sweetbush." All five names capture one or another distinctive trait. The flower stalks are leafless and therefore wirelike; the dense cluster of stems is reminiscent of sweetbush; the dried stems of late summer look like tufts of straw; broken stems and leaves exude milky sap; and the root system is not very well developed.

Wire lettuce, although not edible, is related to ordinary garden lettuce. Both belong to the Liguliflorae, a subfamily characterized by milky sap and heads composed entirely of ray flowers. The pale pink or lavender-pink heads of wire lettuce are scattered along side branches. The achenes (dry, one-seeded fruits) bear tufts of fine, light brown bristles that act like parachutes, catching in the wind and taking the seeds away.

This species grows on plains and slopes, often in disturbed sites, where it is an early colonizer. Few individuals live longer than twenty or thirty years.

Hopi women were said to apply the plants internally and externally to promote milk flow when nursing. Chemical analysis has confirmed the usefulness of many folk medicines. Using wire lettuce to stimulate milk flow, however, might be an instance of the "doctrine of signatures," the ancient belief that plant traits indicate potential uses.

Desert willow

Chilopsis linearis
(Cav.) Sweet

Bignonia Family
Bignoniaceae

Although this graceful, twenty-foot tree is called "desert willow," no true willow has big pink and lavender flowers or elongated seed pods dangling like brown ribbons from the canopy. Desert willow actually belongs to a mostly tropical family that includes a number of ornamentals such as catalpa and cat-claw vine.

In habit and habitat, desert willow is the desert equivalent of true willows. It survives where true willows cannot by a complement of arid-adapted characters. The roots extend deep into the ground—fifty feet or more—in search of water. A waxy coating on the leaves retards water loss. If summer temperatures rise too high and summer drought extends too long, desert willow can drop its leaves and become dormant. Summer or early autumn storms break dormancy, and the trees sprout new leaves. This second crop falls when nights turn cold.

The flowers appear in spring and sometimes again in summer. Large, black carpenter bees are the main pollinators. Diving into the flowers in search of nectar, they can exhaust the supply within a few hours.

Strawberry hedgehog

Echinocereus engelmannii
(Engelm.) Lemaire

Cactus Family
Cactaceae

This long-spined cactus gets its common name from the fruits, which are as red as strawberries when ripe. Immature fruits are bristly with small, sharp spines that hinder the pecking, gnawing, and nibbling of small animals. Mature fruits are spineless or nearly so, virtually inviting packrats, mice, and birds to partake of the sweet flesh and tiny, black seeds. Some seeds pass unharmed through animal digestive tracts, and a small number of those land where they can germinate and become established.

Strawberry hedgehog branches profusely, forming many-stemmed clumps. An old plant might have as many as sixty stems. Flowering is in spring. After good winter rains, a single stem might produce a dozen blossoms over the course of a week or two. The flowers are large and brilliantly colored—sometimes magenta or hot pink, sometimes purplish or lavender. Inside the flower, a mass of stamens surrounds the pistil and its green stigma lobes. Visiting bees usually land on the stigmas, then dive into the stamens. They become thoroughly dusted with pollen grains that they carry to the next flower they visit. Each flower sits atop a large green ovary containing numerous tiny green ovules that, if fertilized, will develop into seeds.

Like cactus flowers in general, those of strawberry hedgehog close at the end of the day. If a number of bees have visited a flower during its first day, thus fertilizing most of the ovules, the flower need not open again. But, if fertilization was poor, the flower can open a second and even a third day, thus increasing its chances of producing a large number of good seeds.

Mojave mound cactus

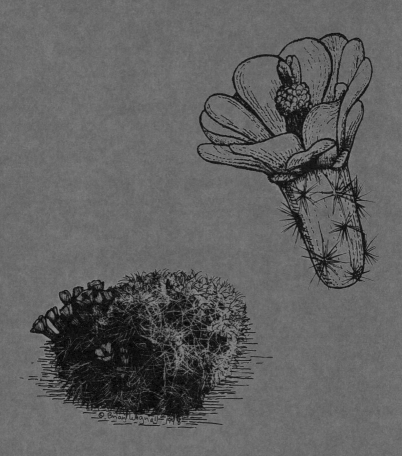

Echinocereus triglochidiatus
Engelm.

Cactus Family
Cactaceae

Mojave mound cactus, as its name suggests, grows as a dense mound of rounded stems, sometimes hundreds in a single clump. The plants can be found in a variety of habitats, including cliff ledges and rocky or gravelly slopes. Hummingbirds are the main pollinators, and it is clear that Mojave mound cactus is adapted to their needs. The flowers are red to orange, a color that hummingbirds associate with nectar, and their funnellike shape provides easy access to the nectar inside. Moreover, the plants bloom in spring about the time that hummingbirds are migrating through the desert to woodlands and forests farther north. Claret cup, another name for this species, refers to the distinctive shape and color of the flowers.

Barrel cactus

Ferocactus cylindraceus
(Engelm.) Orcutt

Cactus Family
Cactaceae

Some people call barrel cacti "compass barrels" because they lean toward the south as they age, a result of faster growth on the south side. The habit can be their literal downfall; eventually the largest plants lean so far that they topple to the ground, uprooting themselves.

By the times it reaches three to four feet in height, a full-grown barrel cactus is about forty to fifty years old. The odds are that most seeds will never get to this point. The heavy rains required for germination happen about once or twice in a decade, for one thing. For another, many seedlings and young plants die during drought or are eaten by rabbits and rodents. As they mature, barrel cacti become nearly invincible. Their water storage capacity is large enough to get them through the worst droughts, and their formidable armature of straight and curved spines deters most animals, no matter how thirsty.

Beavertail

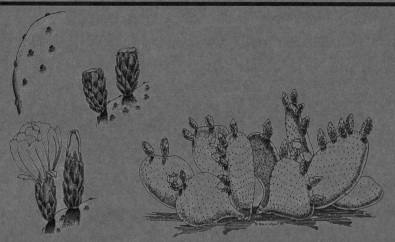

Opuntia basilaris
Engelm. & Bigel.

Cactus Family
Cactaceae

Beavertail is a low cactus with flat, bluish or purplish pads. Although the plants do not have the long spines characteristic of most cacti, they are abundantly furnished with glochids, tiny barbs clustered in fuzzy bunches. These barbs detach from the plant at the slightest touch but can be extracted from your skin only with some difficulty.

Appearing in spring, the magenta- to rose-colored flowers of beavertail are as beautiful in real life as they are on postcards and calendars. Large native bees pollinate the blossoms. Newly formed pads appear in spring as well, bearing tiny triangular leaves that last only a month or so. The new pads and flower buds exude dots of nectar that attract swarms of ants. The ants collect the nectar and prey upon insects that might otherwise chew or suck the cactus pads.

Beavertail is well adapted to extremely hot, arid environments. Like all cacti, it employs a particular mode of photosynthesis that involves taking up carbon dioxide from the atmosphere at night. Carbon dioxide and water, of course, are turned into the sugars needed for growth. Most plants take up carbon dioxide during the day, opening up microscopic pores called stomates to do so. Because the stomates must be open for carbon dioxide to diffuse into the plant, water can and does diffuse out of the pores at the same time. Clearly, photosynthesis places desert plants at risk of losing too much water. By opening their stomates principally at night, cacti evade this risk to some extent. During the summer dry season, beavertail does not open its stomates at all, a further means of reducing water loss. When the soil is wet from winter rains, the plants open their stomates during the day as well as at night, photosynthesizing as much as possible before the long summer drought begins.

Sclerocactus polyancistrus
(Engelm. & Big.) Britt. & Rose

Cactus Family
Cactaceae

Reaching a height of just eight to twelve inches, the single stem of a Mojave fishhook can be easily overlooked, but when it flowers in spring, the plant leaps out of its camouflage, flaunting three to five rose-purple or magenta flowers, each nearly as wide as the stem itself.

The stem surface is nearly invisible under a shaggy coat of spines. Each spine cluster, borne at the tip of a nipple-like protrusion called a tubercule, comprises ten to fifteen white radial spines and nine to eleven reddish-brown or white central spines. Most of the central spines are hooked at the tip, a trait referred to in the species name *polyancistris*, which is Greek for "many fishhooks."

Despite this spiny exterior, small mammals manage to gnaw at the plants for the moisture inside. By starting at the base where the spines are old and brittle, a rodent can eventually hollow out the entire plant. This is a major cause of death for mature Mojave fishhooks. Another is removal by cactus collectors despite the fact that all cactus species in California are protected by law. Collection of Mojave fishhook is particularly unfortunate, because the plants do not do well in cultivation and often die.

Arizona lupine

Lupinus arizonicus
(S. Watson) S. Watson

Pea Family
Fabaceae

If there is a heaven for lupines, California must be it. Of the two hundred species of lupines, seventy-one occur within the borders of the state, and about a dozen can be found in the Mojave Desert. Arizona lupine is a common annual in sandy washes. The pale purplish-pink flowers spiral around the tips of the flowering stalks. Lower on the stem are the five- to seven-fingered leaves so characteristic of lupines. The leaves and stems are rather succulent.

Lupines are adapted for pollination by bees. The large, uppermost petal, called the banner, catches the bee's attention; the two wing petals at either side of the banner provide a landing spot for the bee; and the two petals inside the wings enclose and protect the stamens and pistil in a boat-shaped arrangement called the keel. Only a strong insect, such as a bumblebee, can force the wing petals downward to gain access to the pollen and nectar inside the keel. The creamy splotch on the banner of Arizona lupine flowers is a nectar guide that directs the bee to the reward inside. Once a flower has been pollinated, the spot changes from cream to red-violet, a color that bees do not see. The result is that bees are attracted only to unpollinated flowers.

Erodium cicutarium
(L.) L'Her.

Geranium Family
Geraniaceae

Filaree, also called heron-bill, is one of the earliest annuals to bloom in the spring and often colors acres of desert a delicate lavender. The tiny flowers are five-petaled and grow in groups of two or three at the tips of slender stalks. After the petals fall, the ovary elongates into a slender, green sword. The fernlike leaves form rosettes on the ground.

Filaree seeds literally plant themselves. The swordlike fruit curls into a corkscrew as it ripens. When rainfall moistens these corkscrews, they uncurl, and the spiraling motion drives the tips of the fruit into the ground.

A native of Europe that has been widely naturalized in the United States, filaree was introduced into California in the eighteenth century by the Spaniards. It spread to other states by various means, including sheep, which inadvertently transported the corkscrews on their woolly backs and legs. Browsing animals eat the foliage, and ants collect the seeds. It is not uncommon to see ant mounds wreathed with the dried brown husks of the fruits.

Purplemat

© Brian Wignall 1998

Nama demissum
A. Gray

Waterleaf Family
Hydrophyllaceae

Like many annual wildflowers in the desert, purplemat accommodates itself to the weather. In years of plentiful winter rain, the plants bear scores of small, trumpet-shaped flowers on ground-hugging stems. The masses of deep pink or red-violet flowers make brilliant splotches on sandy or gravelly flats and washes. Narrowly spoon-shaped or elliptic leaves crowd around the flowers, and a few more leaves are scattered along the stems. When rains have been poor, however, an entire plant might consist of one flower with a subtending leaf or two. In this way, plants can set seed and perpetuate the species even in unfavorable years.

The seed capsule is no more than a quarter-inch long and contains numerous miniscule seeds. Their tiny size is a clue to their fate. Such small seeds are adapted to escape the attention of ants and mice by sifting down through grains of soil and coming to rest in a dark, dry place. There they wait (sometimes for several years) for the right combination of moisture and temperature. They will not respond to summer rain, if there is any, because the soil is too warm. Only a good soaking in fall or early winter enables purplemat seeds to germinate.

Krameria grayi
Rose & Painter

Ratany Family
Krameriaceae

White ratany, a spreading shrub about two feet tall, looks like many desert plants in its thorn-tipped stems and gray foliage. Unlike most desert shrubs, however, white ratany is parasitic. It attaches itself to the roots of common shrubs like creosotebush and triangle-leaf bursage and siphons off a portion of the food they manufacture for themselves. It also takes water and perhaps other nutrients from its hosts.

Ratany flowers have glossy, red-violet sepals and inconspicuous petals. Two of the petals, having been highly modified in the course of evolution, are actually glands. Whereas most flowers offer nectar as a reward for pollinators, ratany offers oil. Bees in the genus *Centris* collect the oil and combine it with pollen from other plants, then use the mixture as food for their larvae.

White ratany is locally common on gravelly plains and rocky slopes. A similar species, *Krameria erecta* Schultes, known as range ratany or Pima ratany, also occurs in the Mojave Desert. It differs mainly in the type of prickle on the plump seed pods.

113

Desert paintbrush

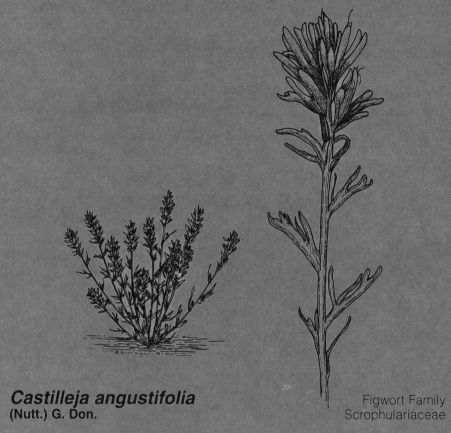

Castilleja angustifolia
(Nutt.) G. Don.

Figwort Family
Scrophulariaceae

Even expert botanists have difficulty in telling apart the 200 species of paintbrush in western North America. The flowers themselves are inconspicuous: it is the bright red bracts beneath each flower that catch the eye. Most, if not all, species of paintbrush are hemiparasitic, requiring host plants to supply water and nutrients. The seedlings grow poorly or die if not attached to the proper host (often perennial grasses). As is the case with most hemiparasites, paintbrush plants lack a well-developed root system. Instead, they have conducting tubes called haustoria that attach to the roots of the host. The Figwort Family contains many hemiparasites, including owl's clover, another desert wildflower.

Desert paintbrush is a perennial of rocky slopes. The stems are gray, the leaves long and narrow. The bright red (or sometimes yellow-orange) bracts have three to five lobes at the tips. Directly above each bract is the flower, a slender greenish tube with a long beak. The fruits are dry capsules containing numerous fine seeds.

=© Brien Wignall 1997 =

Mimulus bigelovii
(A. Gray) A. Gray

Figwort Family
Scrophulariaceae

Desert monkey flower, a spring-blooming annual of rocky slopes, gravelly flats, and sandy washes, cuts its coat to suit the cloth. When little soil moisture is available, a plant might grow no taller than an inch and bear only one or two flowers; in better years, stem length and flower number increase in proportion to the moisture available. Either way, the trumpet-shaped flowers seem huge in comparison to the slender, reddish stems. The lobes of the flowers are deep pink or red-violet. Their golden throats, spotted with maroon, make a vivid contrast that attracts pollinators and guides them to nectar at the bottom of the tube.

Desert five-spot

Eremalche rotundifolia
(A. Gray) E. Greene

Mallow Family
Malvaceae

The cup-shaped flowers of desert five-spot are marked inside with traffic signals–a dark maroon spot at the base of each pink petal. This is where nectar is secreted. Native bees quickly learn to associate the dark spots with nectar, and that is where they go when they visit the flower. At the center of the flower is a complicated structure that looks like a miniature bottle brush. The filaments of numerous stamen unite to form the handle of the brush, and their anthers make the bristles. Styles and stigmas poke out the top. As a bee collects nectar from one flower, it brushes against the anthers and picks up pollen; in visiting the next flower, the bee inadvertently deposits some of that pollen on the stigmas, thus pollinating the flower.

Eremalche, the genus name of desert five-spot, is Greek for "lonely mallow" and was bestowed by Edward L. Greene, an Episcopal minister and a botanist who lived in the late nineteenth century, a time when deserts were little frequented except by wild animals and the occasional miner, making them lonely places for human beings indeed.

Sphaeralcea ambigua
Gray

Mallow Family
Malvaceae

Several species of globemallow are common in the desert. Most have scalloped leaves and peachy-pink flowers. Coulter globemallow (*Sphaeralcea coulteri* (Wats.) Gray) is a spring-flowering annual of sandy soils. Emory globemallow (*Sphaeralcea emoryi* Torrey) is a bushy perennial of roadsides and rocky slopes. Its red-orange to lavender flowers are crowded on the main stem. Apricot mallow, the most drought-tolerant of desert globemallows, also grows on rocky slopes and roadsides. Its purplish-pink or apricot-colored flowers are the largest in the genus. The thick leaves, typically ridged on the underside, set apricot mallow apart from the others.

Globemallows can be somewhat prickly from stiff hairs on leaves and stems. If you get the hairs in your fingers, then happen to rub your eyes, you might discover to your regret why globemallows are sometimes called "sore-eye poppies." Both the Seri Indians and the Akimel O'odham treated diarrhea with a drink made from the pounded root and boiling water. The root has emollient properties and has also been used to treat skin infections.

Sand verbena

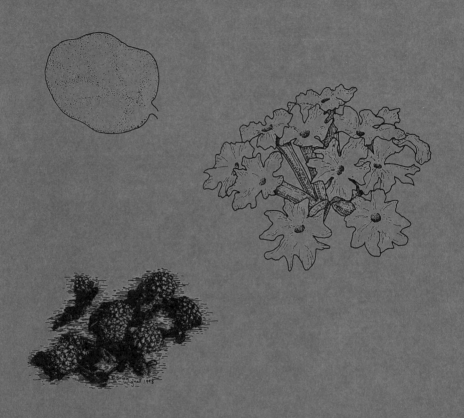

Abronia villosa
Wats.

Four O'Clock Family
Nyctaginaceae

Sand verbena, a sprawling annual of dunes and sandy flats, often makes a colorful patchwork with dune evening primrose, woody bottle washer, spectacle pod, and other spring-blooming, sand-loving wildflowers. The long tubes of the sweetly scented, magenta flowers ensure that only insects with equally long tongues can reach the nectar inside. Because the flowers are most fragrant at night, moths are probably the major pollinators. The broad wings of the seed pods catch readily in the wind, dispersing the seeds.

©Brian Wignall 1998

Allionia incarnata
L.

Four O'Clock Family
Nyctaginaceae

A common annual in gravel along roads and on dry slopes, trailing four o'clock blooms sporadically from spring to fall, usually after rains. The hot-pink or white blossoms vary in size: during hot, dry weather, they might be no larger than shirt buttons; given plenty of moisture, they can be as big as quarters. Each scalloped blossom is really three flowers combined in a single flower-like head. Some species in the Four O'Clock family have flowers that really do open around four o'clock. Those of trailing four o'clock open around sunrise and close about midday, except in cloudy weather, when they might stay open all day long.

Scarlet bugler

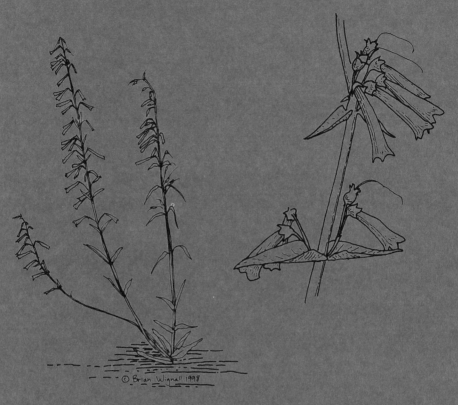

© Brian Wignall 1998

Penstemon eatoni
A. Gray

Figwort Family
Scrophulariaceae

Scarlet bugler is one of about forty species of *Penstemon* that are polli-nated by hummingbirds. Its inch-long flowers are tailor-made for that pur-pose. Birds can see red but bees cannot; therefore the red flowers of scar-let bugler appeal to hummingbirds and are usually overlooked by bees. Two-lipped, more-or-less trumpet-shaped flowers are characteristic of the Figwort Family; in scarlet bugler, the lips are not obvious, having been modified to lengthen the floral tube. This modification allows hummingbirds to hover unimpeded at the flowers, whereas butterflies and bees, which must perch to feed, can find no convenient foothold.

Scarlet bugler can be common on rocky slopes and along roads at a wide range of elevations, from pine forest down to desert. The stems die to the ground after the seeds disperse, but the roots are perennial, and new shoots appear the following year. In the desert, scarlet bugler blooms in spring.

Palmer penstemon

Penstemon palmeri
A. Gray

Figwort Family
Scrophulariaceae

The wand-like, waxy stems of this perennial wildflower can reach five or six feet in height. The large, triangular leaves are also waxy. They do not have stalks but clasp the stem instead. Flowers are large and pale pink. Their wide mouths reveal a slender style and stigma, four functional anthers, and a single nonfunctional anther called the staminode. The genus name *Penstemon* means "almost a thread," a reference to the staminode, which is readily recognizable as a flat, narrow tongue covered with golden hairs.

The bell-shaped flowers of Palmer penstemon evolved to accommodate large-bodied bees such carpenter bees and bumblebees. As a bee enters a flower, anthers dust its back with pollen. When the bee goes to another flower of Palmer penstemon, the drooping stigma picks up pollen grains. Purple lines on the inside of the pale pink flowers guide bees to nectar in the short tube.

This perennial wildflower blooms in late spring.

Spanish needles

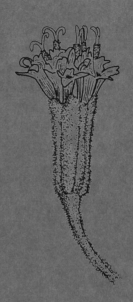

Palafoxia arida
B. Turner & M. Morris

Sunflower Family
Asteraceae

Spanish needles gets its name from the one-seeded fruits, or achenes, which are half-inch-long, four-angled "needles." Each achene bears seven triangular scales at its apex. The flowers, nine to twenty per head, are white or pale pink. Dark green or blackish phyllaries surround the flowers in each head, cupping them tightly until the ovaries have ripened into achenes. The narrow leaves and erect, much-branched stems are rather dark, too. Spanish needles is an annual up to two feet in height; the common type in the Mojave Desert is variety *arida*. The plants can be abundant along roads and on sandy soils in spring and, if there have been warm-season rains, in autumn as well.

Another type of Spanish needles, variety *gigantea*, is found outside the Mojave Desert on active sand dunes. It greatly resembles variety *arida* except that all its parts—stems, leaves, flowers, achenes—are twice as large. This tendency toward gigantism, as it is called, is not uncommon among plants of sand dunes and is probably an adaptation to active sand. Whereas the relatively small variety *arida* could easily be buried by blowing sand, the much larger variety *gigantea* has a better chance of keeping its flowers aboveground where pollinators can see them.

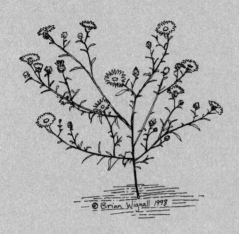

© Brian Wignall 1998

Machaeranthera canescens
(Pursh) A. Gray

Sunflower Family
Asteraceae

As far as asters are concerned, many have been called over the years but few have been chosen. Hoary aster, also known as desert aster, is one of the rejects. When he first described this species in the nineteenth century, Frederic Pursh, a German botanist, called it *Aster canescens* in reference to the gray-haired pubescence. Several decades later, Asa Gray, a well-respected botanist and professor at Harvard University, examined hoary aster and its closest relatives and, on the basis of bract size and number, decided that they all belonged in the genus *Machaeranthera*. The upshot is that most true asters have large, soft leaves and thrive in moist or shaded situations, whereas the rejected asters, those species in the genus *Machaeranthera*, have small, tough leaves and grow in dry habitats. Hoary aster is not to be confused with Mojave aster (also called desert aster), once placed in the genus *Aster*, then in the genus *Machaeranthera*, but now in the genus *Xylorhiza*. Like hoary aster, Mojave aster has purple ray flowers but can be distinguished easily by the magnificent two-inch-wide flower heads.

In the Mojave Desert, hoary aster is an annual or a short-lived perennial with small (less than an inch in diameter) flower heads. The ray flowers are an aster-like purple (sometimes white), the disk flowers predictably yellow. The gray-haired leaves are narrow and can have smooth or toothed margins. Stems can grow to twenty inches in height but in dry years may be much shorter.

Mojave aster

Xylorhiza tortifolia
(Torr. & A. Gray) E. Greene

Sunflower Family
Asteraceae

This beautiful wildflower bears two-inch-wide flower heads on long, leafy stalks. Yellow disk flowers crowd the center of the head, surrounded by as many as sixty ray flowers that can be lavender, violet-blue, pinkish, or white. The narrow leaves are toothed, each tooth tipped by a weak spine.

Blooming mostly in spring, sometimes in autumn, Mojave aster, also called desert aster, can be common on dry, rocky slopes. It is one of a group of three closely related species, all restricted to arid regions. Mecca aster (*Xylorhiza cognata* (H. M. Hall) T. J. Watson), a shrub up to five feet in height, is known only from Riverside County, California. Unlike Mojave aster, which is woody at the base only, Mecca aster is woody-stemmed throughout. Orcutt's woody aster (*Xylorhiza orcuttii* (Vasey & Rose) E. Greene), which closely resembles Mecca aster, is restricted to San Diego and Imperial counties, California. Mecca and Orcutt's asters are rare and should not be disturbed in their wild habitat.

Caterpillars of the desert checkerspot, an orange springtime butterfly, eat the foliage of Mojave aster and one or two other spring-blooming wildflowers. Checkerspot caterpillars sport gray and orange stripes on a black background, which should make them easy to recognize, if not easy to see; this striking combination of colors fools the eye into perceiving bars of sunlight and shadow instead of the outline of a caterpillar's body.

Desert lupine

Lupinus sparsiflorus
Benth.

Pea Family
Fabaceae

Desert lupine is a spring-blooming annual that is locally common in the Mojave Desert. It can easily be recognized by its blue, white-dotted flowers and by the seven- to eleven-fingered leaves. The flowers are on short stalks along the stem, an arrangement called a raceme. As many as ten species of bees, including bumblebees and honey bees, visit the flowers for pollen or nectar. After the flower has been pollinated, these rewards are no longer available. The white dot on the uppermost petal turns magenta at that point, informing bees that the flower is not worth visiting again.

When ripe, the pods explode and fling their seeds some distance away. The seeds germinate on as little as a half-inch of fall or winter rain, so even in years when the wildflower display is poor, you might be able to find masses of desert lupine on highway shoulders. The plants also grow mixed with other winter annuals on rocky slopes.

Another species called desert lupine, *Lupinus shockleyi* S. Watson, somewhat resembles *Lupinus sparsiflorus* but has leaves that are grayish underneath and green above, and, in addition, has yellow rather than white spots on the purplish-blue flowers. It grows in sandy areas.

Indigo bush

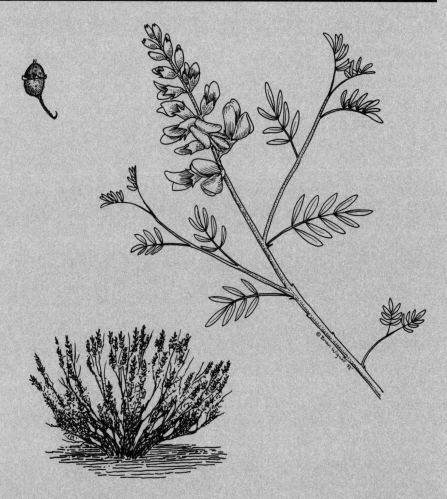

Psorothamnus fremontii
(Torr.) Barnb.

Pea Family
Fabaceae

A shrub to four feet in height, indigo bush is stiffly branched but not especially thorny. The stems of older plants are often picturesquely gnarled or twisted. When it flowers in spring, indigo bush is one of the most beautiful shrubs of the Mojave Desert. Ranging in color from dark blue to deep purple, the silky blossoms contrast vividly with the whitish, zigzag stems. Often the flowers appear while the stems are leafless. The small leaves, divided into several pairs of leaflets, drop during periods of drought and cold. Indigo bush thrives on gravelly plains and rocky slopes.

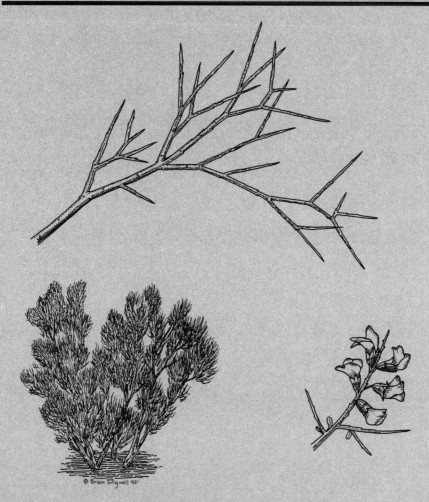

Psorothamnus spinosus
(A. Gray) Barnb

Pea Family
Fabaceae

It is said that this small tree looks like a puff of smoke in a desert wash, hence the common name. Smoke tree can be found in sandy washes at low elevations. The branches and trunks get their characteristic gray or silvery color from dense, fine hairs pressed against the stem.

The dark purple to deep blue flowers appear in June and early July at the hottest, driest time of year. Only extreme drought can keep smoke tree from flowering. Seeds disperse in summer and germinate during the winter rainy season.

Notchleaf phacelia

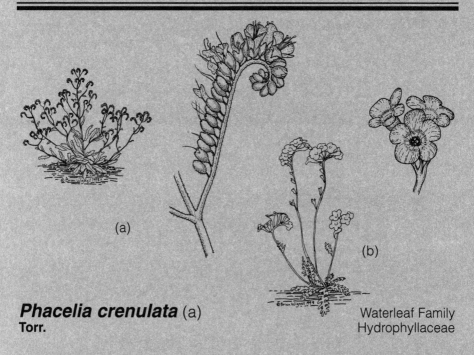

(a)

(b)

Phacelia crenulata (a)
Torr.

Waterleaf Family
Hydrophyllaceae

Yellow throats
Phacelia fremontii (b)
Torr.

Notchleaf phacelia, a common spring-blooming annual, flourishes on rocky slopes, along roadsides, and in sandy washes. The bell-shaped, lavender to purple flowers grow on stems that curl under like the scroll of a violin. The interior of the flower is white. The leaves can be scalloped or deeply cut into lobes. As they age, the stems often turn reddish-brown. Leaves and stems might feel damp or sticky to the touch; under magnification you can see the glandular hairs that are responsible for the moistness. These same hairs give some people an itchy, red dermatitis much like poison ivy. Especially when crushed, the plants smelly unpleasantly skunky.

Yellow throats, also called Fremont phacelia after John C. Fremont, its discoverer, is another stinker. It too flowers in spring and can be common on sandy or gravelly flats. The funnel-shaped flowers have yellow tubes and pink, blue, or violet mouths. The fernlike leaves are mostly clustered at the base of the plant.

Phacelias are sometimes called wild heliotrope. That name, however, is probably best reserved for the true heliotropes, which belong to the Borage Family.

Palmer phacelia

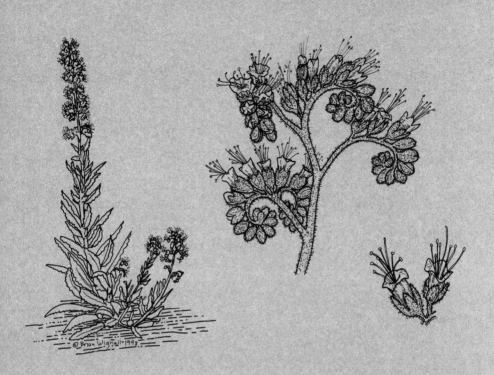

© Brian Wignall 1998

Phacelia palmeri

Waterleaf Family
Hydrophyllaceae

Thickly crowded with pale blue flowers and toothed leaves, the main stem of Palmer phacelia can reach two feet in height. The plants taper from a wide base to a narrow, curled apex, giving them a peculiar resemblance to a miniature fir tree. The stems and leaves are rough with long, stiff hairs and sticky from glandular hairs. When handled, the plants smell strongly skunklike. Palmer phacelia is a biennial. The plants develop a cluster of basal leaves in the first year and send up a flowering stalk in the second year. Biennials typically die after they shed their seeds.

In the Mojave Desert of Nevada and Arizona, Palmer phacelia grows on gypsum soils. For reasons that are not entirely clear, many desert plants cannot survive on gypsum. Palmer phacelia can, however, and by virtue of its affinity with gypsum substrates, avoids the usual competition among wildflowers for space, water, and nutrients.

Bladder sage

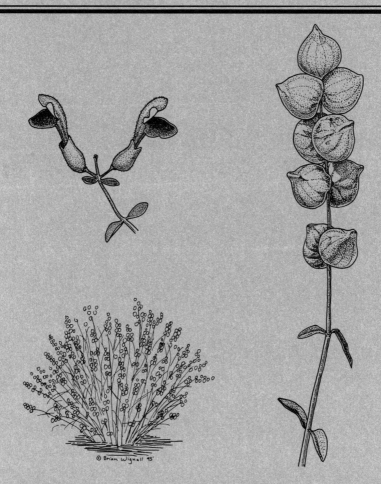

© Brian Wignall '93

Salazaria mexicana
Torr.

Mint Family
Lamiaceae

Bladder sage, also called paperbag bush, gets its name from the fruits, which consist of four hard nutlets surrounded by a papery balloon.

The slender, flexible branches are borne in pairs along the main stems. When present, the leaves are sparse, giving the five-foot-tall shrubs a markedly twiggy appearance. The violet flowers appear in spring and sometimes again in autumn. They are tubular, with an upper and lower lip.

Bladder sage is most common in washes, where it is subject to occasional floods; it also grows on gravelly flats and rocky slopes, often coming in after disturbance.

© Brian Wignall 1998

Salvia columbariae
Benth.

Mint Family
Lamiaceae

Chia, a spring-flowering annual, has tiny blue flowers aggregated in tight spheres, one or two per stem. The stem seems to pierce these flower heads as a skewer pierces a cube of beef. Like most members of the Mint Family, chia has square stems. Most of the leaves are clustered at the base of the plant. On the upper surface, they are incised in a grid, giving them a crinkled appearance. Rounded bracts subtend the flower heads.

Blue sage

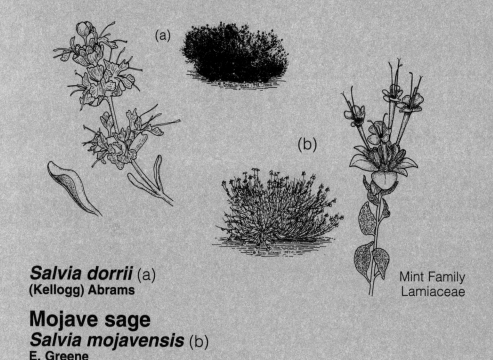

(a)

(b)

Salvia dorrii (a)
(Kellogg) Abrams

Mint Family
Lamiaceae

Mojave sage
Salvia mojavensis (b)
E. Greene

Blue sage, a spreading, much-branched shrub about one or two feet in height, can be found in many different plant communities including Joshua tree woodland and sagebrush scrub. Leaves may be round or spoon-shaped. Either way, they are whitish or silvery from a dense covering of scales. Clustered in heads, three or four heads per stem, the half-inch-long flowers are blue and two-lipped. As the flowering stalk ages, the individual heads tend to blend. Occasional plants have whitish, lavender, or pinkish flowers.

Mojave sage also has blue flowers clustered in heads, but the heads are borne singly at the stem tips and the flowers are twice as long. Mojave sage is often more than two feet in height, and its ovate, green leaves are puckered and deeply veined.

Bees are probably the most important pollinators of these two species, and the flowers provide every facility for bee visitors. The lower lip of the flower makes a landing platform. The upper lip is bent upward, giving the bee plenty of room in which to maneuver. An incoming bee typically lands on the lower lip, grasps the edges of the flower, then pushes her head between the lips. As the protruding style brushes her back, the stigma picks up pollen from the last flower she visited.

Desert larkspur

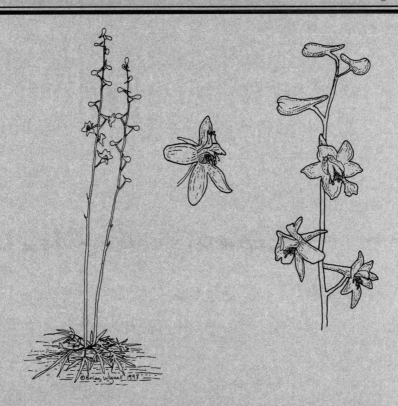

Delphinium parishii
Gray

Crowfoot Family
Ranunculaceae

Sometime between autumn and early spring, the roots of desert lark-spur, buried among rocks in desert canyons, send up a cluster of long-stemmed leaves. When spring days begin to warm and lengthen, a flower-ing stalk shoots up among them. If the autumn has been very dry, neither leaves nor flowers will appear; instead, the roots wait unseen for a better year.

The sky-blue flowers have five large sepals, the uppermost modified to form a spur, and five inconspicuous petals. Leaves are generally round in outline and deeply cut into lobes. Larkspur is tailor-made for bee pollination. The blue color is a favorite of bees, and only a strong insect, such as a bum-blebee, can push apart the petals to get at the nectar. In foraging for nectar, bumblebees become dusted with pollen to carry to the next blossom. Larkspurs hide their nectar in the spur to protect it from insects that are not legitimate pollinators. A small insect might otherwise crawl into the flower and sip the nectar without pollinating the stigmas.

Broomrape

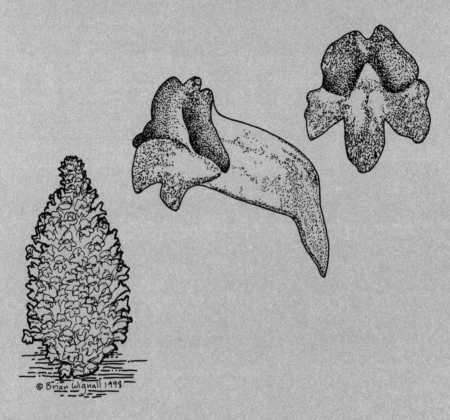

© Brian Wignall 1993

Orobanche cooperi
(Gray) Heller

Broomrape Family
Orobanchaceae

Broomrape, a parasite, depends entirely on its host plants for sugars, water, and nutrients. Like most other parasites, broomrape lacks true roots and attaches itself to its hosts by special conducting tubes called haustoria. Shrubs in the Sunflower Family, particularly the bursages (*Ambrosia* spp.) and the burrobushes (*Hymenoclea* spp.), are usually the hosts. Secretions from the roots of host plants stimulate broomrape seeds to germinate. The need for special secretions keeps the seeds from germinating on the wrong host or in the absence of a host altogether. Broomrape is seldom abundant, an indication of how infrequently the seeds manage to locate a suitable host. Ants might bury some seeds close to host-plant roots, thus fostering germination. Also, broomrape often grows in sandy places such as dunes and washes where the sorting and sifting activities of wind and water might deposit seeds near the roots of likely hosts.

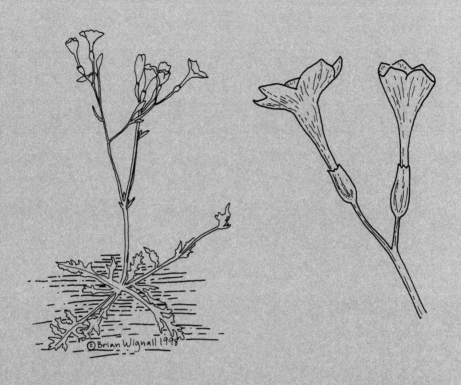

©Brian Wignall 1998

Gilia scopulorum
M. E. Jones

Phlox Family
Polemoniaceae

More than a dozen species of gilia can be found in the Mojave Desert. Most are delicate spring-blooming annuals with a rosette of fernlike or feathery leaves and a single slender flowering stalk that branches toward the top. Rock gilia grows in shaded, rocky ravines. Its inch-long, trumpet-shaped flowers have a purple tube, a yellow throat, and a pink or lavender rim. This color scheme is common to many species of gilia, including star gilia (*Gilia stellata* A. A. Heller), which embellishes the yellow throats with purple dots, and broad-leaved gilia, *Gilia latifolia* S. Watson, which has leaves that are toothed rather than finely divided. Flowers of sinuate gilia (*Gilia sinuata* Benth.) have no yellow at all: the tubes and throats are purple, the lobes pink, lavender or white. Foliage also helps to distinguish among the many desert gilias. Leaves of broad-leaved gilia are strongly scented and somewhat skunky. Rock gilia has translucent hairs on the leaves. Leaf hairs of star gilia are white and sharply bent. Cobwebs enmesh the leaves of sinuate gilia.

135

Turpentine broom

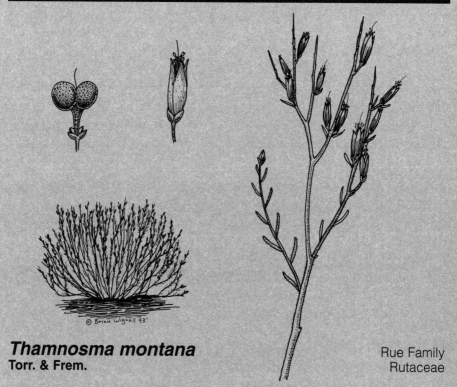

© Brian Wignall 93'

Thamnosma montana
Torr. & Frem.

Rue Family
Rutaceae

People sometimes mistake this green and usually leafless shrub for mormon tea. A quick whiff of the crushed stem will alert them to the difference: mormon tea has little odor; turpentine broom has a sharp and pungent scent. The smell originates in the small, round glands that dot the stem. Turpentine broom belongs to the same family as citrus; you can see similar glands on the rinds of oranges and leaves of orange trees.

Caterpillars of the black swallowtail (*Papilio polyxenes coloro*), a rather large black and pale yellow butterfly, eat only turpentine broom, and unless she makes a bad mistake, that is the only place where the female swallowtail lays her eggs. Just as we can recognize turpentine broom by smelling it with our noses, she can tell it by tasting it with her feet. By tapping stems or leaves, she performs a quick bioassay that tells her whether a plant is turpentine broom or something else altogether.

Flowering from late winter through spring, this low shrub is one of the earliest bloomers in the desert. Turpentine broom can flower in autumn, too, given enough summer rain. The deep purple flowers, stacked one above the other on the tapering, green stems, look like tiny flasks. Later in the year, the two-lobed fruits are equally conspicuous. Slender leaves appear with the flowers but fall once the soil dries out.

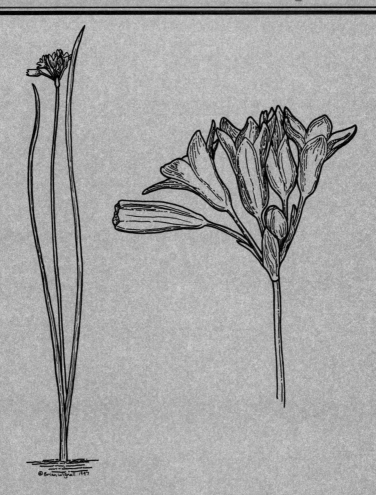

Dichelostemma capitatum
Alph. Wood

Lily Family
Liliaceae

Growing on rocky slopes in oak woods, chaparral and desertscrub, wild hyacinth can be abundant in spring if autumn and winter rains were plentiful. At the top of the single flowering stalk are two to fifteen flask-shaped flowers. The shape of the inflorescence is variable, and the flowers can be crowded into a globular head or borne on short stems that radiate from the stalk like the spokes of a wheel. Blue, lavender, purple, or sometimes white, the flowers are of six more or less identical petals. Other common names for wild hyacinth are bluedicks and covena; early settlers called it grass nuts because of the edible bulbs.

Suggested Reading

No field guide can include every plant in an area as rich in plant species as the Mojave Desert. Users with some training in botany will find the following works indispensable for identifying Mojave Desert wildflowers.

Benson, L. *The Cacti of the United States and Canada.* Stanford: Stanford University Press, 1982.

Benson, L., and R. A. Darrow. *Trees and Shrubs of the Southwestern Deserts*, Third edition. Tucson: University of Arizona Press, 1981.

Hickman, J. C., ed. *The Jepson Manual: Higher Plants of California.* Berkeley: University of California Press, 1993.

The discussions of desert plant ecology in this book are based on a variety of technical books and articles. Readers who want to learn more about plants of the Mojave Desert might find the following books of interest:

Bowers, J. E. *Dune country: A Naturalist's Look at the Plant Life of Southwestern Sand Dunes.* Tucson: University of Arizona Press, 1998.

Tweit, S. J. *Seasons in the Desert: A Naturalist's Notebook.* San Francisco: Chronicle Books, 1998.

Zwinger, A. H. *The Mysterious Lands.* New York: Dutton, 1989.

Index

Note: **Latin names are in bold italicized type**; *Latin family names in italicized type;* common names and English family names in regular type

141

Acknowledgements

Upon accepting the job as illustrator of this book I had no idea how far I would have to go to get the necessary photographs to portray the unique plants and flowers of the Mojave Desert. I am indebted to the following people for all their efforts on my behalf. Each and every one of these people went the extra mile, literally, to make this much-needed book come to fruition.

First I would like to thank Alan Romspert of the Desert Studies Consortium, California State University System, for taking me into the Mojave on two separate occasions for twelve-hour days of locating and identifying dozens of plants. I would also like to thank the team of professionals that Alan called on to help locate plants: Jim Andre, Co-Director of the Sweeney Granite Mountains Desert Research Center, Gina Robinson of the Southwest Natural and Cultural Heritage Association, and Adrienne Knute, author of *Plants of the East Mojave*. These people were not only hound dogs in the field of botany but were genuinely delightful individuals to meet and get to know. Their intensive search got me through one-third of the plants needed for this book.

The group of people who took me to the half-way mark are: Jim Holland, Jane Rogers and Deanne Coulson of Joshua Tree National Park, and Kevin Emmerich of Death Valley National Park. The great variety found in each of these parks is what made their contributions so necessary to the book.

Finally, I would like to thank Wesley Niles, professor of Botany at the University of Las Vegas, and Pat Leary, Biologist at the University of Southern Nevada, for providing the final slides to complete the book.

The Mojave Desert is a place of beauty and diversity. It is a wonder to me that so many kinds of flora and fauna can survive in what at times can be harsh or even severe conditions. I hope this book will help guide you when you venture into the fascinating plant world of our Mojave Desert.

Brian Wignall, Artist and Naturalist